A Guide to
BATS
of Britain and Europe

A Guide to
BATS
of Britain and Europe

Wilfried Schober
Eckard Grimmberger

Consultant Editor Dr Robert E. Stebbings

HAMLYN

Picture credits
97 colour photographs by A. Benk (pp. 26, 48), J. Červený (pp. 164, 182 upper), J. Gebhard (pp. 162 lower, 165), K.G. Heller (pp. 99, 182 lower), O.v. Helversen (pp. 142, 162 upper), A. Limbrunner (pp. 6/7, 80/81), P. Morris (p. 14), D. Nill (pp. 3, 32, 184/185), R.E. Stebbings (pp. 46 lower, 47, 72, 79, 94), G. Storch (p. 15) and M.D. Tuttle (p. 13). All other colour photographs by E. Grimmberger. *73 black-and-white photographs* by J. Červený (1), J. Gebhard (2), E. Grimmberger (66), H. Hackethal (3) and O.v. Helversen (1). *29 black-and-white drawings* by T. Schneehagen and 20 sonagrams.

Front cover: Mouse-eared bat (Stephen Dalton/NHPA).
Title page: Bechstein's bat.
Page 6/7: Pipistrelle in old great spotted woodpecker hole.
Page 80/81: Lesser horseshoe bat in hibernaculum.
Page 184/185: Mouse-eared bat colony.

This English edition published in 1989 by
The Hamlyn Publishing Group Limited,
a Division of the Octopus Publishing Group,
Michelin House, 81 Fulham Road,
London SW3 6RB, England

Copyright © 1987, FRANCKH'SCHE
VERLAGSHANDLUNG, W. Keller & Co.,
KOSMOS-Verlag, Stuttgart
Copyright © 1989 English translation, The
Hamlyn Publishing Group Limited

Original title: Die Fledermäuse Europas
Translated by Iain and Ingrid MacMillan (Worcestershire Bat Group) and adapted for the English language by Dr Robert E. Stebbings

ISBN: 0 600 5642 4X

Typeset by Tradespools Limited, Somerset, England
Produced by Mandarin Offset
Printed in Hong Kong

Preface

There are approximately 980 different species of bats and flying foxes. They mainly occur in the tropics, with only 30 species occurring in Europe. There are still relatively few people who have any detailed knowledge of these mysterious night-time creatures which 'see' with their ears and fly with their 'hands' and hang themselves up by the toes of their hindlegs to sleep. The history of human civilization is full of the most absurd reports about these mammals and even today various media exploit the 'vampires' in order to strike fear into people's hearts.

It is true that the many peculiarities in the lives of bats have contributed to the fact that they were, and still are, subject to prejudice, scorn and even extermination. Today, however, it is not man's superstition and fear which threaten the existence of bats. Instead, it is the progress of civilization and industrialization that is posing an ever-increasing threat to the survival of these animals. It is therefore of vital importance to make a strong effort to ensure the conservation of these useful animals.

Becoming involved with bats requires knowledge of the individual species. Although the number of bat species occurring in Europe seems small, it can be difficult for the amateur, and in some cases even for the expert, to distinguish between some species. There are only a few publications that can be easily understood by the interested layman. We hope that with this book we will be able to provide both an insight for a wider audience into the fascinating results of modern bat research and an introduction to the European bat species in words and pictures. Finally, an identification key is provided to help recognize any species found.

We particularly wish to express our gratitude to all those friends and colleagues who have helped us with expert advice, the supply of pictures and literature, have collected materials and who have supported many excursions, some of them joint. Our special thanks go to Dr J. Gaisler (Brno), Dr H. Hackethal (Berlin), Prof. Dr v. Helversen, Drs K. Heller and R. Weid (Erlangen), as well as to Dr Zd. Bauerová (Brno), A. Benk (Hannover), M. Bogdanowicz (Bialowieza), J. Červený (Prague), B. Evtimov (Peštera), J. Gebhard (Basel), Dr J. Haensel (Berlin), G. Heise (Prenzlau), Dr U. Jüdes (Kiel), M. Masing (Tartu), W. Oldenburg (Waren), Zb. Urbańczyk (Poznán), Prof. Dr Y. Tupinier (Caluire) and M. Wilhelm (Dresden).

Our warmest thanks go to Mrs T. Schneehagen (Leipzig) who with great skill produced the excellent illustrations.

Wilfried Schober   *Eckard Grimmberger*

Contents

PREFACE   5
THE LIFE OF BATS   7
Bats – vampires, devils or
   gods?   8
Fifty million years on earth   11
They fly with their hands   16
Where do bats live?   25
Hunting prey by
   echolocation   31
Echolocation – the sixth sense
   of bats   36
Harems and nurseries   42
The social behaviour of
   bats   52
Hibernation – life in
   suspended animation   57
Migration to frost-free
   winter quarters   68
Ringing   70
PROTECT OUR BATS!   73
WHICH BAT IS IT?   81
European bats, in words and
   pictures   82
Horseshoe bats
   (*Rhinolophidae*)   86
Vesper bats
   (*Vespertilionidae*)   103
Free-tailed bats
   (*Molossidae*)   181
**IDENTIFICATION KEY TO
EUROPEAN BATS**   185
Identification key to fami-
   lies   186
Pictures relating to identifi-
   cation key   196
Sonagrams   210
Tables   214
BIBLIOGRAPHY   220
INDEX   223

The life of bats

Bats – vampires, devils or gods?

Even today, bats still evoke fear, shock and disgust. If the reasons for these reactions are examined, it becomes clear that only very few people have any detailed knowledge about the appearance and way of life of these animals. Like all nocturnal creatures, such as owls, bats have occupied the human imagination from time immemorial. For centuries they have suffered from a bad image in many parts of the world. Thus as long ago as ancient Rome, Divus Basilius wrote: 'The bat is by its nature the devil's blood relation.' In the Baroque period too, the bat was regarded as the symbol of the Antichrist and therefore of the devil. This explains why Christian art often depicts the devil and his hellish companions with bats' wings, whereas angels are shown with birds' wings. The Spanish painter Goya used bats as a symbol of threat and unreason and even today, film and television are still haunted by Count Dracula in the shape of a blood-sucking vampire.

Supernatural powers have been ascribed to bats: the witch doctors of various primitive races used them as part of their amulets; the books of ancient Arab doctors contain numerous prescriptions which use either whole bats or parts of bats; and the medieval 'quack doctors' of Europe frequently included them in their 'remedies'. In India, flying bats are still today sold in bazaars for medical purposes. Their fresh skins are removed and applied to the diseased parts of the body.

Since nothing was known about the ability of bats to navigate using ultrasound until approximately 50 years ago, it was commonly assumed that bats had night vision. Even some medical recommendations were based on this inference, such as those which can be found in the book *The Wonders of the World* by Albertus Magnus (13th century): 'If they wish to see something in the darkest night and if nothing is to remain hidden from them during daylight, then they should rub their faces with the blood of bat and everything will occur as I have said.'

The ability of bats to fly, accounts for the fact that for centuries they were regarded not as mammals but as birds. In the Bible (Leviticus chapter 11, verse 18) the faithful are thus admonished: 'Among the birds, these are the ones you may not eat: ...the hoopoe, the bat.'

Enlightened people, however, such as the painter and scientist

In Christian art, devils are depicted with bats' wings (Rila Monastery, Bulgaria).

Leonardo da Vinci, perceived bats differently. In the construction plans for his flying machine he pointed out that the bat's wing had to serve as a model. One of his drawings clearly shows that the shape of the wings and the finger-like struts are reminiscent of bat wings.

Some cities, such as Valencia in Spain, considered bats worthy of inclusion in their coat of arms. Kurfürst Friedrich der weise von Kursachsen granted the painter Lucas Cranach the elder the right to bear as his coat of arms '...a golden shield, with a black snake inside with two black bat wings in its middle...'.

Outside Europe, bats often had a very different and much more positive significance to mankind: in the ancient cultures of Central America, bats played an important role in religious history. One of the Mayan deities was depicted as a human with extended bat wings and a bat's head. Images of this figure can be found on stone columns and earthenware pots which were excavated in the vicinity of two-thousand-year-old temples. In the hieroglyphs of the Mayas too, the bat symbol occurs frequently. In China and Japan bats have always been a symbol of happiness. The Chinese word 'fu' means 'bat' as well as 'good fortune'. A common talisman is a type of coin depicting a tree

9

Medallion on a Chinese robe from the 18th century. Its ornamental design shows five bats surrounding the tree of life. They represent the concepts of health, wealth, happiness, longevity and a peaceful death.

with roots and branches as a symbol of life. The tree is surrounded by five bats ('wu fu') with outspread wings. To the bearer of the talisman, they promise health, wealth, happiness, longevity and a peaceful death.

Today bats are enjoying a gradual increase in popularity. Nevertheless, many humans still express repulsion or indifference towards them and the unfounded fear that bats can get entangled in women's hair is hard to eradicate. Now as before, bats are being killed, poisoned or fumigated. It is still not widely known that bats are harmless and indeed very useful animals in their capacity as 'biological pesticides'. Bats are endowed with a number of abilities and characteristics that are unique in the animal world: they are the only mammals capable of active flight and use their 'hands' to do this; they 'see' with their ears; suspend themselves head-down by the claws of their hindfeet; and can reach the truly biblical age of 30 years (compare this to other small mammals which live only a few years).

Bats have lived on earth for well in excess of 50 million years. During that period they have conquered many ecological niches and have evolved undisturbed by man. However, during the last 40 years man has been responsible for drastic changes in the environment, particularly in the highly industrialized countries.

This has brought the continued existence of many species under increasing threat, with bats being amongst those species especially affected. It is essential that everybody strives towards the conservation of these charming and useful animals. To achieve this, a more thorough understanding of the bats of Europe is of great importance. Bats are legally protected in all European countries except a few small islands such as the Isle of Man and the Channel Islands.

50 million years on earth

The book *Historia Animalium* written by the 16th-century Zurich naturalist Konrad Gesner contains the following passage: 'The bat is an intermediate animal between bird and mouse, so that it can fittingly be called a flying mouse; although it can be classed neither as a bird nor a mouse for it has the appearance of both.' It was a long time before bats were assigned their rightful scientific position in the animal kingdom. A superficial examination will reveal various characteristics which are common to both bats and mice. Many European species especially have a body size, fur colour or ear shape very similar to those of mice. This comparison with mice which appears again and again is also reflected in the naming of bats: greater mouse-eared bat (*Myotis myotis*), the French 'chauve-souris' (naked mouse) or the English 'raremouse'.

However, bats simply are not flying mice but an autonomous order of mammals with the scientific name of Chiroptera (hand-wing). This order, which is surpassed in number of species only by the rodents, is characterized by one important common feature: the adaptation of the forelimbs into wings.

Approximately 250 years ago, the Swedish biologist Carl Linnaeus began what was then the first comprehensive survey of animals, plants and rocks. In his work *Systema Naturae* (1735) he developed the concept of 'species' and classified all living creatures according to their assumed family relationships. Linnaeus, who at that time knew only six species of bat, two of them from Europe, was misled by the characteristics of their teeth and at first classed them as predatory animals. As new criteria kept emerging, it is not surprising that 30 years later Linnaeus classified bats amongst the apes, on the basis that the mammary glands on their chest were an important characteristic. The knowledge of bats was immensely increased by expeditions which collected many new species during the following 100 years. This explains why by 1865 the zoologist Koch refers to over 300 species in his work *Essential Characteristics of Chiroptera with a Particular Description of the Bats Occurring in the Duchy of Nassau and Bordering Regions.*

The discovery and description of new species continues even today. Approximately 15 years ago a great stir was caused by the discovery of a new species of bat which also proved the founder member of a new family. This species, with the name of *Craseonycteris thonglongyai*, has a body weight of approximately 2 g and a body length of 29–33 mm, which makes it the world's smallest mammal apart from the Etruscan shrew (*Suncus etruscus*). Some insects, such as our native stag-beetle (*Lucanus cervus*), are distinctly larger and heavier than this, with the males reaching lengths of up to 80 mm. Amongst the largest representatives of the order Chiroptera is the widespread fruit-eating Kalong (*Pteropus vampyrus*), a member of the suborder of flying foxes and an impressive creature with a wingspan of up to 1.70 m and a weight of up to 900 g. Amongst European bats, the extremes are represented by the pipistrelle bat (weight 3–8 g, wingspan c. 200 mm) and the greater mouse-eared bat (weight 20–40 g, wingspan up to 450 mm). Only the rare greater noctule exceeds the mouse-eared bat in size (weight 40–75 g, wingspan 410–460 mm).

The evolution of this order of mammals over millions of years has given rise to an immense variety of forms. There are approximately 980 recognized species worldwide. It is likely that the main reason for this wealth of species lies primarily in the ability to fly. The same can be said for birds and insects. The mainly nocturnal lifestyle of bats and their conquest of the air space made it possible for them to exploit habitats and food sources (ecological niches) unavailable to other ground-dwelling mammals or to birds which tend to be active during the day.

All bat species occurring in Europe are insectivorous. Usually they do not begin to forage until dusk or nightfall. Amongst our native insectivorous birds, the nightjar (*Caprimulgus europaeus*) is the only one which hunts for its food at night. The diet of tropical bats is much more varied: there are fruit-eating bats and 'flower bats' that feed on nectar, thus contributing to the pollination of blossoms; there are some species that have specialized in preying upon smaller bats, mice and other animals; and there are bats that catch fish or frogs.

Well-known, at least by name, are the vampire bats occurring in Central and South America. Their best-known representative is the species *Desmodus rotundus*. This usually feeds on the blood of domestic animals but occasionally it also feeds on human blood. Its sharp teeth inflict small wounds in the skin and the bat licks up the blood which flows out. The loss of blood itself is minimal and usually causes no harm. However, the

Vampire bat (*Desmodus rotundus*).

danger from vampire bats is that they can transmit rabies and other diseases.

Most of the bat species mentioned that have specialized in a particular prey are also nocturnal which helps to avoid competitors and predators, but there are bats that hunt for insects by day, such as the African yellow-winged bat (*Lavia frons*).

Taxonomists have divided the Chiroptera into 18 families (see Table 2, page 216). Some families are made up of only one species, whereas the vesper bat family numbers approximately 320 species. Bats are divided into two large suborders. The first includes the Megachiroptera, mainly large species known as 'flying foxes'. Approximately 175 species have so far been described which live in the tropics and sub-tropics of the Old World. The second suborder consists of the Microchiroptera which are mainly small species.

The ancestors of bats were four-legged mammals; the possession of wings was a secondary acquisition. No mammal occurring today can be considered as an ancestor of the bat, not even those that have specialized as 'gliders'. Even today it is

Fossilized bat (*Archaeonycteris trigonodon*) from the oil shale pit at Messel near Darmstadt, West Germany. The Messel fossils are estimated to be 50 million years old. This specimen is in the Senckenberg Museum in Frankfurt.

unclear either how bats have evolved into active fliers or in what stages this development took place. To gain some idea of what their ancestors may have looked like, one has to go far back in the earth's history.

Fossilized remains, such as those from the oil shale pit at Messel near Darmstadt, prove that bats existed in the same form as today as far back as 50 million years ago. Examinations carried out on the fossils to discover the structure of the internal ear and larynx showed that even then bats orientated themselves by means of ultrasound. Bats are therefore a very old but also highly specialized order of mammals.

Insectivorous mammals, such as hedgehogs and shrews, are regarded as the most primitive placental mammals. Their ancestors can also be considered as the ancestors of the other placental mammals. It is therefore highly likely that bats evolved from prehistoric tree-dwelling insect eaters. Apart from the

Flying fox (*Rousettus stresemanni*). The large eyes indicate the good night vision of the Megachiroptera.

ability to fly and the later adaptation to new habitats or new sources of food, many bat species still retain what some regard as primitive characteristics. These relate to either the construction of the skull, the shape of the dentition, the digestive system or the degree of brain development. Of particular importance for the Microchiroptera was the development of the ultrasound echolocation system.

They fly with their hands

The conquest of the air by bats was made possible by the modification of the arm and hand into a wing. The elongated forearm consists only of the powerful radius, the ulna having regressed. The 2nd to 5th middle hand bones and the fingers connected to them have also been elongated. The 2nd finger consists only of one phalanx, the 3rd finger of three phalanges and the 4th and 5th fingers of two phalanges. The cartilaginous tips of the fingers end in a T-shape at the edge of the wing membrane. The thumb has retained its normal shape and remained short. It has a sharp claw which enables bats to climb well, even upside down. Most flying foxes also have a small claw on the 2nd finger, but this is largely redundant.

The flight membrane (patagium) stretches from the side of the body, between the fingers, across to the tips of the wings and down to the tail. The tail of most European bats is almost completely incorporated into the membrane, one exception being the European free-tailed bat (*Tadarida teniotis*) in which most of the tail extends beyond the rear edge of the membrane. Horseshoe bats have a relatively shorter tail than vesper bats and fold it onto the back when at rest. Vesper bats fold the tail onto the stomach whilst the free-tailed bat generally extends it.

The edge of the tail membrane is additionally stiffened and supported by a calcar made of bone which is attached to the ankle joint. Depending on the nature of the flight manoeuvre and tension of the tail membrane, the calcar lies either laterally to the foot or is splayed out from it. In some genera, for example *Nyctalus*, a stiff flap of skin (post-calcarial lobe) occurs on the calcar. This flap is supported across its middle by a T-shaped piece of cartilage which emanates from the calcar.

The hind legs of bats have several functions. They are mostly incorporated into the membrane as far as the foot and are used during flight to spread or fold together the tail membrane. The claws of the back feet are used to hang from when resting. The leg is rotated upwards and outwards in the knee joint, and the foot and its claws point backwards, not forwards as is the case in other mammals. This makes hanging on walls possible. A special locking mechanism allows the claws to grip whether the muscles are relaxed or not, so even dead animals may remain hanging.

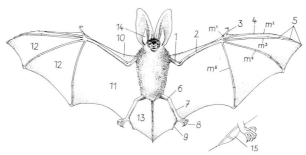

Diagram of the flight membranes and associated skeleton. Skeleton and wing membrane parts: 1. humerus, 2. forearm, 3. thumb, 4. metacarpals (m1, m2, m3, m4, m5), 5. phalanges, 6. femur, 7. tibia and fibula, 8. foot, 9. calcar (without post-calcarial lobe), 10. antebrachial membrane (propatagium), 11. lateral membrane (plagiopatagium), 12. wing membrane (chiro- or dactylopatagium), 13. tail or interfemoral membrane (uropatagium), 14. tragus, 15. calcar with post-calcarial lobe and support.

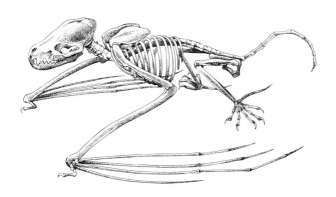

Skeleton of a mouse-eared bat (based on Grasse, 1955).

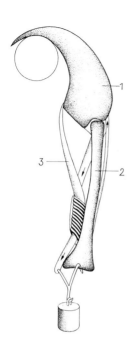

The claws of the back foot are kept in a tight grip by the weight of the hanging bat acting on the tendon. The resting bat can thus hang effortlessly from a branch or other projection (based on Schaffer, 1905). 1. Claw, 2. phalanx, 3. tendon.

When resting, the vesper and free-tailed bats fold their wings together so that the wing membranes are barely visible. The length of the folded wing in most vesper bats is shortened by the phalanges of the 3rd to 5th fingers folding backwards against the metacarpals. By supporting themselves on their wrists and thumbs as well as their backward pointing feet, the vesper bats can raise their body off the ground, run rapidly and even jump and move sideways or backwards. When climbing head first, the thumb claws are used alternately. Vesper bats can even climb backwards and, by using their back feet, climb up overhanging surfaces.

In narrow cracks bats can be observed climbing up by wedging themselves between two surfaces. In contrast, horseshoe bats are relatively helpless on the ground. Once there they cannot lift up their body and walk but can only progress forwards by a series of leaps. Horseshoe bats are therefore always found hanging and never resting or walking on a flat surface. When they are hanging free, however, they can move around with small steps on a rough surface. In addition, they usually need a roost access hole which is large enough to fly through. When resting, the greater and

The barbastelle bat (*Barbastella barbastellus*) has a rapid and agile flight.

Flying Natterer's bat (*Myotis nattereri*). Echolocation calls are transmitted through the open mouth.

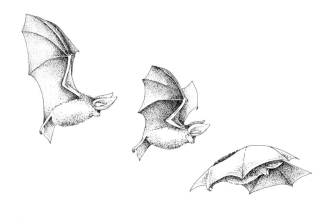

lesser horseshoe bats fold and wrap the wing membrane around themselves like a coat. In contrast, the Mediterranean horseshoe bat bends the fingers in the joint between the 1st and 2nd phalanges by 90–180° and folds the wing membrane in this area together. The body is thereby not completely enveloped. As well as fly, climb, run and jump, bats can also swim, albeit not voluntarily. If a bat does accidentally fall in the water, it swims by spreading out its wings. Sometimes a bat can take off from the water surface.

The shape of the wing reveals the type of flight and the flight capability of a bat: the long, narrow wings of a fast flying species contrast strongly with the broad wings of a slow flying species. In flight the wings perform a rotational-like movement. The tail membrane is used to aid in-flight manoeuvres and to act as a brake on landing. The pectoral skeleton of the bat is very strong in relation to the small pelvis. To improve the anchorage of the flight muscles, a bat's sternum, like that of birds, has a bony projection called a keel.

Flying uses a lot of energy and the flight muscles, especially, require a considerable supply of oxygen. In order to meet the energy requirements, which are four times higher in flight than at rest, considerable demands are placed on the circulatory and respiratory systems. To cope with the considerable increase in heart beat and rate of respiration, the heart has special adaptations and is three times larger than is normal for a non-flying mammal of equivalent size. Thus the heart can pump

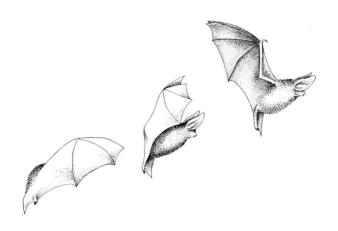

Schematic diagram of the wing movements of a hovering long-eared bat (based on Norberg, 1976).

more blood through the body at any given time to feed the muscles with the necessary oxygen. Here there is another adaptation: whilst in many mammals the absorbative capacity of blood for oxygen is 18% by volume, it reaches 27% in bats. Work by the body produces heat and the bat's body temperature increases in flight. Since bats neither sweat like humans nor pant like dogs, a clever cooling system prevents a dangerous increase in body temperature. When the body temperature increases, a special system of valves allows the thin blood vessels in the wing membranes to dilate and the resulting increased blood flow is cooled by the cold stream of air which continuously flows over the wings. The flight membrane includes nerves and small bundles of muscles in addition to the blood vessels. The muscles mainly serve to keep the wings taut as the airstream passes over them. The wing membranes, which are almost hairless except for one part of the tail membrane, appear delicate and sensitive, but with their elastic fibres are in fact very resilient and tough. Holes usually repair very quickly.

During the development of the embryo, the wing membrane grows out of folds of skin at the sides of the body. Later the wing bones begin to grow. The wing of the newly born bat is still fairly undeveloped and the hands of the young animal only attain their final proportions during growth outside the mother's body.

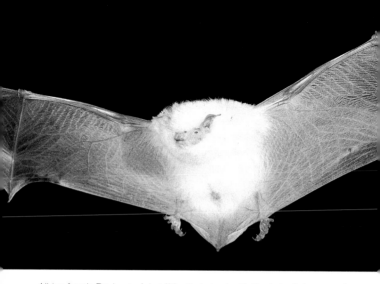

Albino female Daubenton's bat (*Myotis daubentonii*). The lack of pigment makes the blood vessels in the wing membranes easily visible.

Together with the wing membrane, one of the most striking features of a bat is its face. A large bat threatening with open mouth commands respect. Its jaw resembles that of an insect eater, but the large canines give it the appearance of a predatory animal. Noctules, greater mouse-eared and other large bats can easily crunch up the hard shell of large beetles. The number of teeth in European species ranges from 32 (*Tadarida*) to 38 (*Myotis*). Very striking also are the bizarre skin formations around the nose of horseshoe bats. These 'nose leaves' do not occur in any of the vesper bats or the European free-tailed bat.

The ears of bats are of varying shape and size and their length ranges from 9–13 mm in the pipistrelle bat to a maximum of 42 mm in the brown long-eared bat. All vesper bats have a tragus in the ear whilst this is absent in the horsehoes. The differing shape and size of the ear and tragus is a very useful character for identifying bats.

Bats have relatively small eyes, which in all species appear dark (or black). Long-eared bats have the largest eyes in relation to their size whilst the barbastelle has very small ones. The eye-lids have no eyelashes. When the eyes are closed, the narrow eye-lid slit can hardly be distinguished. A few strong sensory hairs are found on the muzzle of vesper and horseshoe bats, and in the latter also on the nose leaf. Skin glands located around

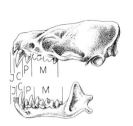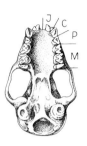

Skull of the serotine bat (*Eptesicus serotinus*) viewed from the side, above and below (**I**, Incisors; **C**, Canines; **P**, Premolars; **M**, Molars). The teeth are well developed, pointed and partially cusped. They are reminiscent of the jaw of a carnivore. The pointed canines hold the prey and the sharp molars grind up the chitinous shell.

the mouth exude a fatty secretion which is used for maintaining the wing membranes in good condition during grooming. The secretions probably also contain odorous substances which act as signals to other bats of the same species.

Bats' fur, in contrast to most other mammals, contains no woolly element and contains only one type of hair. Some genera or species have a hair structure which is so characteristic that it can be used as an aid to their identification. Many bats have hair of two colours. The underside is in all species lighter in colour than the fur on the back. Young animals are in general darker and duller in colour than the adults. In some species the colour of the fur also changes somewhat after the moult in the autumn. (The differing colouring of the fur is best illustrated in the colour photographs of the individual species shown in the second part of the book.) On their hindfeet, most bats have stiff, bristle-like hairs, although these may not always be obvious. The Natterer's bat has a fringe of stiff, hooked hairs on the trailing edge of the tail membrane.

The sex of a resting bat cannot be determined by appearance alone. European bats do not exhibit any sex differences in coloration, as do birds, for example. However, females are on average slightly larger than males. The penis is easily visible. During the mating period the testes and epididymis become

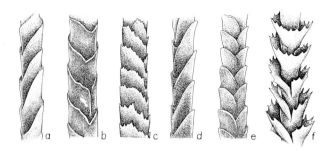

Different surface structures of the hairs of a number of bat species: **a.** lesser horseshoe bat, **b.** Natterer's bat, **c.** Nathusius' pipistrelle, **d.** barbastelle bat, **e.** noctule bat, **f.** European free-tailed bat. The middle section of the hair is illustrated in each case (based on Tupinier, 1973).

clearly visible in many species, so that it is possible to determine their readiness for mating. The females have a pair of mammary glands which are located near the armpits. (An exception amongst the European bats is the parti-coloured bat which has two pairs of mammary glands.) The teats of lactating females are easily visible. Horseshoe bats have an additional pair of false teats near the groin which the young grip onto with their teeth.

Where do bats live?

All European bats need roost sites which protect them against climatic effects, such as cold and rain, as well as against predators or disturbance. Since bats do not build nests they depend upon suitable existing roost sites.

Different roosts are used during the year relating to changing needs. The major types are: winter roosts, day and transitory roosts, nursery roosts and mating roosts. The last three types are often referred to under the rather imprecise term 'summer roost'. Winter roosts are used by bats for hibernation and large numbers of different bat species often use the same site. The largest hibernaculum currently known in Europe is the bat reserve Nietoperek near Miedzyrzecz in West Poland. There, about 50 m below ground, more than 25,000 bats of 12 different species hibernate in a vast system of concrete tunnels dating from the Second World War.

After hibernation, bats move to roosting sites where, usually separated according to species, they often stay for only a few days, but occasionally remain for several weeks. Individual bats, or sometimes small groups, are found in these day or transitory roosts. The bats leave these roosts nearly every night to hunt for food. Such roosts are occupied by the bats when they move from their hibernaculum to their summer roosts. Nursery roosts are the sites shared by either small or large numbers of female bats, often over a period of several months. Here they give birth to and raise their young. During this time, the males of many species live on their own in day roosts, although the males of some species, such as parti-coloured or noctule bats, occasionally form large colonies.

After the nurseries have dispersed, male and female bats come together to mate. There is usually no distinction between mating roosts and day roosts. In the case of bats resident in Northern and Central Europe, the four roost types mentioned above are usually geographically separate. Migratory species travel up to 1000 km or more from their winter to their summer roosts, whereas in southern Europe, with its more favourable climate, one species of bat may spend the whole year in the same site, for example a cave.

In the case of sedentary species, different roost sites are often found in close proximity to one another, even in Central Europe. So, for example, pipistrelle bats hibernate inside a church behind wall plaques or in the cracks of walls, and subsequently occupy

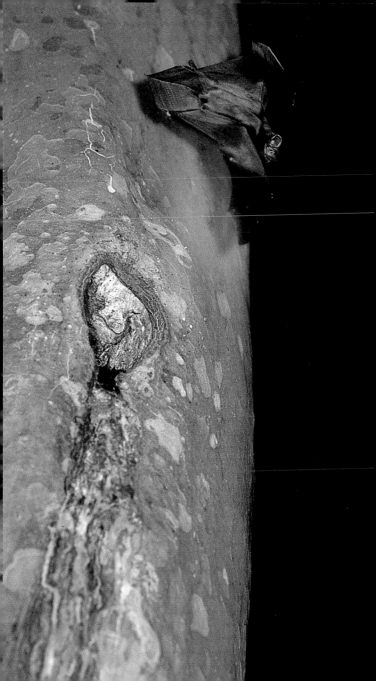

day roosts in the nave roof or cracks in the outer walls of the church. Later the breeding roost may be behind the panelling in the church tower which can be accessed through a crack from outside. Mating then occurs again in the day roost.

Bat roost sites can be further categorized according to the habitats and living quarters used in the summer (Table 1, page 214). House-dwelling bats (anthropophiles) are more or less tied to human settlements. Typical species are the serotine, mouse-eared and grey long-eared bats, and to a certain extent the pond, whiskered and lesser horseshoe bats, and a few other species. Depending upon climatic conditions, a particular species may be house-dwelling in the north of its distribution, but cave-dwelling in the south. So in the north the lesser horseshoe bat spends the summer in warm lofts or underground boiler rooms, whilst in the south it is a cave dweller. As warmth-loving animals, bats could only extend their range northwards by seeking out buildings with a more favourable microclimate. Natural caves in these regions are too cold, in contrast to the 'artificial caves' (i.e. buildings) provided by man which offer more suitable living conditions.

The bats in southern Europe which are predominantly cave- or rock-dwelling bats (lithophiles) include all the horseshoe bats and Schreiber's bat, as well as the lesser mouse-eared bat. Woodland or tree-dwelling bats (phytophiles), on the other hand, are associated with woods throughout their entire range in the summer and some also hibernate in hollow trees. Typical representatives are the three noctule species, the Nathusius' pipistrelle and Bechstein's bats. If the various types of bat roost are looked at more closely, there is a striking variety of suitable sites.

Hibernation sites are relatively uniform and must satisfy the following criteria: the temperature must not, at least in some roost sites, fall much below 0 °C; humidity must be high (up to 100%); there must be little or no draught; and the walls must be rough enough for the bats to cling onto. Also advantageous are additional hiding places such as cracks in the walls, small niches or cavities. Very dirty or dusty sites, including fresh lime or mortar, and soot deposits are avoided by bats. Frequent disturbance, such as the use of a cellar as a storage room, usually drives bats away, but in principle does not exclude the site as a suitable place for hibernation.

In hilly areas, natural caves and old mine shafts are ideal sites for hibernation, whilst in lowland areas suitable substitutes are provided by underground fortifications, old beer and wine

The roost of a noctule bat (*Nyctalus noctula*) in a plane tree. A urine stain running down the tree below the hole is clearly visible.

cellars, former ice cellars, tomb vaults, old bunkers and cellars in private houses. Woodland bats hibernate in hollow trees in which the outer trunk provides at least 100 mm of insulation from the exterior, as well as in deep crevices in rock faces, cracks in walls or smaller cavities in thick-walled buildings or bridges. Individual serotine bats are even known to hibernate in narrow cracks in timber roof beams.

Some species hibernate hanging free from the roof, either exclusively (all horseshoe bats) or predominantly (for example, the mouse-eared bat). In contrast, other species hang on the walls, or seek cracks in masonry, sometimes crawling in loose rock on cave floors; even open pipes or drill holes are used. Other sites where bats have been found hibernating are behind pictures in churches, behind crumbling plaster, under raised layers of rust on iron supports, or on roots growing through the roof of a roost site.

The possible sites for day or transitory roosts are numerous. House-dwelling bats can conceal themselves in roof timbers, under rafters, in cavities of beams or in the ridge. On the exterior of the house, several sites suggest themselves: cracks around window frames, behind weather boarding or hanging tiles, between timber framework and masonry, above the soffit or in hollow walls. If bats get into the living space, they often conceal themselves behind the folds of curtains. When looking for bats in the roof space do not look upwards, but initially examine the floor for droppings. The roosts located above are then easy to find.

Woodland bats have their day roosts in abandoned wood-pecker holes, hollows in old trees, cracks in trees, crevices behind peeling-off bark and wood piles. They readily take to bird nestboxes and special bat boxes.

Cave- and rock-dwelling bats seek out natural caves, mines or cracks in rock faces which are not too cold. There are, however, many atypical day roost sites, such as nesting holes of sand martins (*Riparia riparia*), cracks under bridges, the hollow concrete poles of street lights, ventilation shafts and between the joints of wall slabs of modern blocks of flats.

Nursery roosts are usually more spacious than day roost sites, since they have to accommodate a group of females and young. House-dwelling bats seek out the warmest spots for their nursery roosts in the roof space of private houses, churches or other buildings. They are often found in the ridge of the roof or in the church tower. Romantic ruins with half-collapsed roofs are unsuitable, as the draughts and rain coming in make it too cold. The roofs of buildings with bat roosts must be intact with, of course, an access opening or hole to scramble through.

House-dwelling bats which prefer narrow cracks, find their

Old fortifications often serve as hibernation sites for bats.

Roost sites on the inside and outside of houses and trees.

Collection of bat droppings with dead babies. In the northern part of the mouse-eared bat's range, periods of bad weather prevent mothers feeding and this may cause the death of a large proportion of the babies due to starvation after only a few days of life.

nursery roosts in places such as behind facia boards and weather boarding or tiles. Pipistrelle bats quickly occupy suitable spaces in newly built private houses. Nursery roosts in warm underground rooms, such as underground boiler shafts or cellars, are known to be used by greater and lesser horseshoe and mouse-eared bats.

The nursery roosts of woodland bats are located in spacious hollow trees and in bat boxes. If a hollow tree is inhabited by a large colony of bats over a long period of time, dark streaks of urine can usually be seen at the entrance and droppings collect below the hole. (Bats in hollow trees often betray themselves to the expert by their loud, high-pitched calls.)

The nursery colonies of cave-dwelling bats are likewise in the warmest part of the cave and may contain over one thousand animals. Some species cluster close together, often in large groups, filling domes or niches in the cave roof where hot air is trapped.

All species of bats use alternative roost sites intermittently. Why such a change of roost site occurs is largely unknown. A worsening in the microclimate is surely of significance as are other factors, such as external disturbances, a mass infestation by parasites or a change in the foraging territory because of lack of food. Generally, however, bats return every year to their traditional roosts, both nursery and hibernation sites and these may be occupied over several decades.

Hunting prey by echolocation

European bats are all insectivorous. Different species show preferences in the choice of insects, hunting grounds and hunting behaviour. These differences make it possible for a variety of species to live in the same habitat without competing with each other. Examples of this are the noctule and the Nathusius' pipistrelle bats in woodlands, or the mouse-eared, pipistrelle and grey long-eared bats in areas of human settlement. Knowledge of the ecological differences between species is very sketchy. Detailed research into the way of life of bats will help correct decisions to be made on the required conservation measures.

If a bat roost is watched on a number of summer evenings, it will be found that the bats emerge to hunt at more or less the same time every evening. The start of their emergence is signalled in advance by considerable agitation in the roost which, in the case of pipistrelle bats, is characterized by high-pitched chattering. The animals are then close to the exit hole. During this phase they groom themselves intensively and stretch their wings. Once the first bat has left the roost, the other animals follow at short intervals. The emergence of a one-hundred-strong pipistrelle nursery roost can take up to an hour. It can be delayed by cold weather or even prevented by strong winds or rain. The start of the night's foraging is determined by the time of sunset and the relative intensity of light around the roost.

The fact that different bat species start to emerge at different times is reflected in the old literature, even in the naming of bats. The noctule, for instance, was called the 'early-flying bat' whilst the serotine was referred to as the 'late-flying bat'.

In spring and autumn in particular, bats indigenous to this country can sometimes be watched hunting during the day. It is often the pipistrelles which start hunting in the early afternoon, but noctules and other species are occasionally active by day. It is likely that the lack of food reserves has forced the animals to adapt their hunting behaviour in this way. In the case of noctule bats, however, some day flights may relate to their known migrations, especially in central and eastern Europe.

The duration of foraging flights differs between species and from night to night, and depends upon food availability. Before they start hunting for insects, bats usually visit ponds, streams or other water surfaces to drink. They do this by repeatedly skimming the water surface close enough to dip their mouths briefly into the water. There is no evidence that bats in the wild

Bechstein's bat (*Myotis bechsteini*) drinking.

drink while hanging up or sitting, as they do in captivity, but it certainly seems feasible.

Bats have regular foraging territories, the size and type of which depend upon the species, the time of year and the availability of food. Nyholm in Finland calculated the size of a foraging territory in an open woodland habitat for a whiskered bat to be 240 m^2 compared to 420 m^2 for a Daubenton's bat. Bats often keep to fixed flight paths within these areas and circle around the same patch repeatedly until they have depleted it of insects, whereupon they move to a different patch. If a mass of insects occurs in a particular area, for example near flowering trees, several bats may hunt there together.

The nature of foraging territories themselves is very variable and is determined by the availability of the favourite prey and by the bat's habitat preference. Some woodland bats prefer to forage low over woodland meadows, paths or clearings, and along the woodland edges and rides. Other species, such as the noctule bat, usually hunt above the tree tops or high above lakes and ponds. The Daubentons's bat exploits the rich insect life around the banks of lakes and ponds, hunting just above the water surface. These are also the favourite foraging grounds of barbastelle, Brandt's and pond bats. Bats frequently follow the course of a stream or river while hunting. House-dwelling bats usually forage in villages, on farms, in gardens, above rubbish tips or around street lights which attract insects. Some species, such as the pipistrelle bat, even find sufficient food within large cities.

Bats with long, narrow wings prefer large open spaces. They fly very fast and find it difficult to manoeuvre in a confined space. Typical representatives are the three noctule species, the European free-tailed bat and the Schreiber's bat. The noctule bat can reach a maximum flight speed of 50 km/h, the Schreiber's bat 70 km/h and in the USA the guano bat (*Tardarida brasiliensis*), a relative of the European free-tailed bat, is said to reach up to 105 km/h.

Smaller species, such as barbastelle and Daubenton's bats, can be fast fliers but are more manoeuvrable in confined areas where they fly slowly. All fast-flying species have very short ears, while the ears of some of the slow-flying bat species are very large.

Serotine and mouse-eared bats have long, broad wings suited to their slow hunting flight in open air spaces. In contrast, for hunting in dense vegetation or in areas full of obstacles, short, broad wings are far more suitable. Such species, for example the brown long-eared bat, can search an area flying slowly at a low level and even hover on the spot to pick prey off twigs and leaves, or off the ground. Horseshoe bats are particularly adept fliers, as are long-eared, Bechstein's and Natterer's bats.

Bats locate insects by means of ultrasound, give chase and finally catch them, either directly in their mouth or with their wing membranes which are used like a scoop net. In most cases, the insects are picked out of the membranes directly by the mouth. Sometimes the prey is first caught in the tail membrane which acts like a pouch from which the insect cannot escape. In this pouch and while the bat is still in flight, the prey is manipulated into a position ready for the bat to eat. The insectivorous bats' long sharp canines penetrate and grip the prey, while the broad, multi-cusped molars are used to crush the very hard chitinous shells of beetles.

Most bats eat their prey on the wing. In the case of larger insects, this involves flying around and around a known route without echolocating. Slow-flying species, such as horseshoe and long-eared bats, take their prey to an established feeding site, where they hang and eat the insect's body.

The wings and legs of moths and other insects are dropped and their accumulation is a sure sign of the presence of bats.

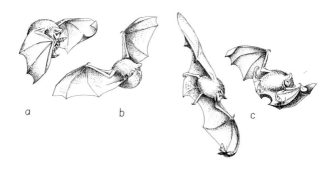

Capturing the prey. (**a**) Generally insects are caught directly in the mouth. (**b**) Larger prey items are often captured in a pocket formed by the tail membrane and from there placed in the mouth. (**c**) If the prey attempts to escape, it is 'caught' in the wing and knocked towards the head.

Several species including the noctule, greater horseshoe and mouse-eared bat have been recorded picking non-flying beetles off the ground. They first use their hearing to locate the beetles and appear then to use their well-developed sense of smell to home in on them. Smell is certainly important to all insectivorous bats as it enables them to distinguish inedible or unpleasant tasting insects. It is not known for certain to what extent some bat species also rely on optical orientation during hunting. Laboratory experiments have shown that the brown long-eared bat does not react to a moth that sits still, but grabs it as soon as it begins to move. Apart from acoustic perception, vision may play a part here.

Little is known about the dietary range of many bats. Because all species thoughout Europe are highly protected, it is not possible to analyse stomach contents by killing bats. Research is therefore restricted to the analysis of food remains. This is relatively easy for some species which leave moth wings at feeding sites. Considerable experience and patience are required to analyse prey from droppings as it involves identifying insects from tiny chitinous fragments. However, this method has shown that bats catch not only moths, beetles, gnats and flies, but also dragonflies, crickets, grasshoppers, caddis flies and some spiders.

In the course of evolution, some of the prey of bats have developed defence systems. Some can partially hear the bat's ultrasonic echolocation and react by simply dropping towards the ground, but there are also moths who themselves emit

Feeding site of the brown long-eared bat (*Plecotus auritus*). In addition to several Noctuid moth species, various butterflies, such as the peacock and the small tortoiseshell, are taken as prey.

ultrasound to signal to a bat that they taste unpleasant. After the first few unpleasant experiences with these insects, a bat usually avoids them.

In summer, a bat's daily food requirement is between one-quarter and one-third of its body weight. For example, a 30 g noctule bat eats about 10 g of food a day. Studies carried out by the Soviet zoologist Kurskow concluded that the maximum daily food intake of bats in the wild was 38% of body weight for the noctule, 31.3% for the parti-coloured bat, 29.5% for the pipistrelle bat and 28% for the barbastelle bat. A single Daubenton's bat, for instance, could eat 60,000 gnats between May 15th and October 15th. Although this is a rather theoretical calculation, it emphasizes the amount of food that bats require. The piles of droppings, sometimes metres high, that accumulate under vast, long-established nursery roosts give some idea of the sheer mass of prey items consumed.

Many species of bats consume large quantities of insects which

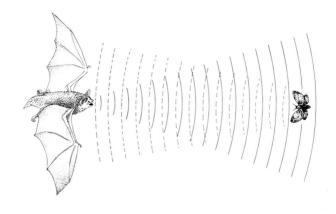

The transmitted sound waves bounce back off the prey and enable the bat to locate the insect.

are harmful to agriculture and forestry. For example, the prey of the brown long-eared bat includes the turnip moth (*Agrotis segetum*), the bright-lined brown-eye (*Polia oleracea*) and the green oak tortrix (*Tortrix viridana*). The role bats once played in combating insect pests is sadly reduced because of the considerable depletion in their numbers across Europe.

Echolocation – the sixth sense of bats

Bats produce easily audible low frequency sounds as well as higher-pitched sounds above the range of the human ear, in the ultrasound range. The audible sounds are very diverse. They may sound like a shrill scolding, a high-pitched squeaking or a chirping, or can resemble the low hum of a large bumble-bee. The noctule has the loudest call among bats. Its shrill, hard metallic calls can be heard for 500 m or more. Like some of the ultrasonic sounds, these calls have a social function and are used to communicate with others of the species. There are also calls that are used for contact between mother and baby, calls that accompany defensive or aggressive behaviour, complaining noises and mating calls with which the males attract receptive females. The discovery of ultrasonic calls and the recognition of their significance only happened fairly recently.

Ever since the 18th century scientists had tried to solve the mystery of how bats avoid obstacles when flying in darkness, but it was not until 1938 that the Americans Griffin and Galambos found the answer. They established that bats emit ultrasonic signals, pick up the returning echo with their ears and so build up an image of their surroundings. Humans and most other mammals navigate with their eyes; we build up an optical image of our surroundings and store it in our memories. Bats, on the other hand, receive an 'auditory image' of their surroundings which is possibly just as exact and just as 'colourful'. Instead of seeing, they 'hear' the entrance to their roosts, the rockface on which they hang up and the prey crossing their flight path. They store this auditory image in their memory and can, in their usual surroundings, automatically avoid an obstacle while 'flying blind'. Whales and dolphins have a similarly effective method of ultrasonic orientation. Cave-dwelling birds, such as the South American oil bird (*Steatornis caripensis*) and Old World cave swiftlets of the genus *Collocalia*, also use echolocation.

The frequency range of bats' echolocation calls is 20–215 kHz. As the number of oscillations per unit time (frequency of the sound) increases the wave length decreases. This is advantageous since the shorter waves provide better detail of small objects. If the signals are converted to a humanly audible frequency, as is possible today using a bat detector in the field, it emerges that many species produce a specific pattern of sound (sonagram) which is characteristic for each species. For example, each sound emission of the vesper bats drops markedly at the end of the call. The call often passes through a frequency range from 100–40 kHz. If we could hear such a call it would not be a pure tone, but resemble a chirp. The emission of a salvo of such chirps has led to the vesper bats being called the 'chirping bats'. These bats are also known as 'frequency-modulating' bats because of the typical frequency modulation (FM) of their ultrasonic calls.

It has been repeatedly confirmed in recent years that the diversity of ultrasonic signals is far greater than was initially envisaged. Many families of bats use quite different systems of echolocation and indeed many use more than one system. It has also been discovered that the horseshoe bats do not emit 'chirps', but produce pure sounds lasting up to 150 milliseconds, with only a short frequency-modulated part at the end. Individual

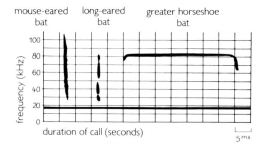

Echolocation signals of various bat species. The vesper bats (mouse-eared, long-eared) emit short frequency modulated (FM) pulses which pass through a wide frequency range within a few milliseconds. The horseshoe bats emit constant frequency (CF) pulses of long duration in a very restricted frequency band. The upper hearing capability of humans is approximately 18 kHz (based on Gebhardt, 1985).

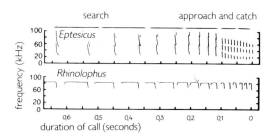

Sonagrams of echolocation signals of vesper bats and horseshoe bats at different phases of hunting. Once the prey is located, the signals become more and more rapid during the approach and catching phases.

species typically have their own specific frequency level of sound production when echolocating. The greater horseshoe bat emits signals at approximately 83 kHz, while the lesser horseshoe uses a frequency of around 107 kHz. Because of the constant frequency (CF) of emitted signal and the short duration of the final frequency-modulated part (CF/FM signals), the horseshoe bats are known as 'constant-frequency' bats.

Our indigenous vesper bats emit their echolocation signals through the open mouth. Exceptions are the two species of long-eared and barbastelle bats which can emit signals through the nostrils with the mouth closed. This is normal for horseshoe bats, which use the movable parts of the noseleaf around the nostrils to concentrate the echolocation signals. By swinging the head from side to side they direct the stream of echolocation signals like a spotlight. The rebounding echoes are picked up by the ears which can move independently of one another.

It is typical of vesper bats with their FM signals that the individual signals are of only very short duration to ensure that the emitted signal and returning echo do not overlap. Sound travels through air at a velocity of 331 m/s. This means that an FM pulse must last no longer than 0.5–1.0 millisecond, if the echo rebounding from an item of prey at a distance of 50 cm is to be heard without interference. The frequency-modulating species determine the distance of the prey item by the time difference between emission of a signal and reception of its returning echo. The direction is ascertained by analysing the difference between the times of arrival of the echo at the left and right ears. The intensity and frequency of the echo are also significant.

The echolocation system of the horseshoe bats is not based on orientation by time differences, since the long CF/FM pulses emitted overlap with the echoes. The horseshoe bats have a filter in their hearing that is tuned precisely to a species-specific frequency. The greater horseshoe bat hears its species-specific echoes of 83 kHz significantly better than frequencies above or below this. Since an echolocating horseshoe bat is flying towards the sound wave echoes from a prey-item or object, the number of waves which it perceives per unit time is increased and the returning sound therefore appears higher in frequency. This effect, named after the physicist Doppler, means that the frequency of the returning echo is higher than the original signal emitted. There is indeed a danger that the sound will be so high in frequency that it will not be heard at all. However, horseshoe bats compensate for this effect; the signals they emit are correspondingly lower so that the echoes received are exactly at the frequency of greatest hearing sensitivity.

If the echolocation signal hits a stationary object, the echo will be pure. A flying insect, on the other hand, modulates the frequency of the echo with its wing rhythm. With their echolocation system, horseshoe bats cannot only correctly determine the direction of the echo, but are even able to detect fine differences in the surface structure of the objects from which the echo returns. A simple experiment shows the sensitivity of this system: a small stone thrown up in the air in a garden where a bat is foraging, will cause it to turn sharply towards the object. As soon as the bat recognizes that the stone is not a prey item, it will turn away without attempting a capture.

The performance of the echolocation system of the horseshoe

bats is markedly better than that of the vesper bats. Experiments have shown that horseshoe bats can perceive wires with a diameter as small as 0.05–0.08 mm. Vesper bats, such as the mouse-eared or long-eared bat, can only detect wires down to 0.2 mm thickness. For this reason horseshoe bats have been caught much less frequently in very fine mist nets than vesper bats. The range of the horseshoe bats' echolocation signals is also superior. Their signals reach to a maximum of 20 m and they can detect prey 8 m away. Vesper bats have to approach to within 2 m of their prey before they can detect it.

There is also a difference between species in the amplitude of the signals. The noctule bat, which hunts in wide open spaces, 'shouts' its echolocation signals into the night at a level of well over 100 decibels, which is comparable to a compressed air hammer. Conversely, species which fly slowly and close to the ground between bushes and trees, such as the Bechstein's and long-eared bat, 'whisper' their signals. When flying in open spaces, bats emit fewer signals than when in locations with many obstacles. Also when bats approach prey, the rate of emitted signals is increased considerably and reaches up to 100 signals per second.

Young bats during the first few days of life can only produce relatively undifferentiated and low intensity signals which serve as contact calls with the mother. The calls of young mouse-eared bats up to the age of 18 days range between 20 and 30 kHz and subsequently rise slowly to between 50 and 70 kHz. Just as children learn to talk, so young bats must learn to echolocate. In some species, the young bat is guided along by the mother in a sort of sound 'umbrella'. Young animals of other species practise alone in or near the roost site while the mother is out hunting.

The subject of echolocation is far more complex than this brief outline can give. A whole range of questions are still waiting to be answered. Largely unresolved is the way that bats orientate themselves over long distances. Research is needed to discover whether they navigate either by the position of the stars in the night sky or by exploiting the earth's magnetic field, or perhaps both. Long distance orientation allows bats to return to their roost even from areas which are unknown to them. Experiments, in which ringed bats were removed from their home areas, have shown that they can find their way back to the roost over distances of 50–60 km.

Let us now turn from echolocation to the other physical

Just before take-off the vesper bats, such as this Brandt's bat, echolocate through the open mouth.

senses. All bats can see. The eyes of most species are small and not very highly developed. They can distinguish differences in brightness and shapes, but they do not possess colour vision.

The sense of taste and smell is well developed. Smell plays an important role in the recognition between mother and baby. Many species use it to find their prey. Unpleasant-tasting prey is spurned by bats after the first few bad experiences.

Perception of temperature is acute and is highly significant for the selection of suitable hibernation sites. The sense of touch is refined by the tactile hairs in the region of the face and the feet. Bats are particularly good at detecting small air currents, an ability which is important when searching for new roosts.

Harems and nurseries

There are still great gaps in our knowledge of the reproductive biology of even some of the European bat species. The mating season begins in autumn after the dispersal of adult females from nurseries, which usually occurs towards the end of August. It includes the hibernation season and lasts until spring. During the mating season the males' testes and epididymis become very prominent. In other seasons they are usually not visible on the outside of the body. Even the facial appearance in some bats changes, such as the male of the Nathusius' pipistrelle bat where the bridge of the nose swells up on both sides.

A stable pairing relationship is unknown in European bats. One male mates with several females and it seems likely that a female can be mated by a number of males. During the mating season, the males of some species, for example noctule and Nathusius' bats, live alone and accumulate a harem of between two and ten females. A male Nathusius' pipistrelle bat may choose, for instance, a bat box as its roost and will stay in it for several days or weeks. It defends its mating roost and the surrounding territory against other males. It then tries to attract females by calling from its box or during flights through its mating territory. It also chases females in flight. Males often keep their mating territory for several years, whereas females change to other territories, perhaps ending up in a different male's harem.

If mating occurs in the hibernaculum the female's role is initially a passive one. Studies of Daubenton's bat have shown that the first activity of a male after awaking from hibernation

Daubenton's bats (*Myotis daubentonii*) mating in their hibernaculum.

is to look for females. It will fly to other bats of the same species, which may be hibernating individually or in groups, land next to or on top of them and start seeking out a female, apparently using its sense of smell. This search is carried out with a lot of energy and persistence and can result in the arousal of a whole group of bats.

Once a female has been found, the male embraces it from behind with its wings and holds it tight. Copulation itself takes place only when the female is slowly awaking from hibernation, but is not yet able to fly. The animals utter shrill calls from time to time and sometimes the male grips onto the fur on the back of its mate's neck with its teeth. The animals remain in the mating position for 20 minutes or longer, during which period copulation may take place several times.

In the case of bats in temperate regions which mate before hibernation, fertilization of the egg does not occur immediately after mating. The female stores the sperm in her reproductive

43

tract and it is kept alive throughout the hibernation period until spring. Ripening of the ovum in the ovary, ovulation, fertilization and the following embryonic development occur only after waking from hibernation. This is a unique phenomenon among mammals. Schreiber's bat is one exception, and achieves the same objective in a different way. The egg is fertilized immediately after mating, but as is the case with deer, seals and badgers the fetal development stops at the blastocyst stage and resumes only in spring. This process is known as delayed implantation because attachment of the blastocyst to the uterine wall and development of a placenta takes place at a later date. In both of these cases, the adaptation guarantees that birth occurs at a favourable season.

If hibernating female bats are taken into captivity and kept warm, fertilization and embryonic development start considerably earlier than in the wild. The babies are born early, even in winter. It is difficult to determine the gestation period in bats as the exact date of fertilization is virtually impossible to detect. Figures range between 45 and 90 days.

Most European bats give birth once a year usually to a single young, but in some species twins and in rare cases three young have been recorded. This is a very low reproduction rate compared with other mammals of the same size (one female house mouse, *Mus musculus*, can give birth to up to 90 young in one year), but it is compensated by a comparatively long life expectancy. Bats can live for up to 30 years, although the average life expectancy is much lower and ranges from about four to six years. Migratory species, such as noctule or Nathusius' pipistrelle bat, are obviously exposed to higher risks than sedentary bats. They make up for their low life expectancy by sometimes giving birth in their first year and by sometimes having twins. About one-third of pipistrelle bats produce young at the end of their first year and this is also the case, if at a lower rate, with the mouse-eared and the lesser horseshoe bat.

In their second year with the exception of the greater horseshoe bat, all individuals of both sexes mate. However, there is always a proportion of females who do not bear young each year. In Great Britain, greater horseshoe bats usually first breed when four years old but some are 7–10 years old before they breed.

From April onwards, females congregate in nursery roosts which can include, depending upon species, up to several thousand animals. Adult males are hardly ever found in these nurseries. The bats in these roosts rarely become torpid during the day since the resultant lowering of the body temperature would delay embryonic development. If prolonged phases of torpor are enforced by cold spells and lack of food, births occur

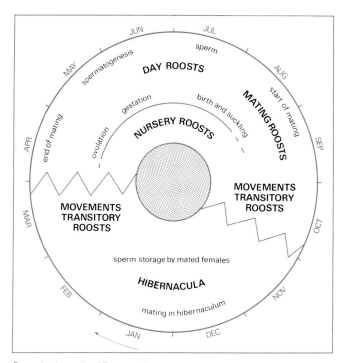

Reproductive cycle of European bats.

later. Births in the nurseries take place over a period of several days to several weeks depending upon the climate and species.

Parturition has been closely watched and described in some bat species, for example by Kolb for the mouse-eared bat and Heise for Nathusius' pipistrelle bat. The majority of births take place during the day. The female separates herself from the other animals and adopts the birth posture. She clings to the surface with all four limbs and hangs either head-down (mouse-eared bat) or in the otherwise unusual head-up position (Nathusius' pipistrelle and pipistrelle bats). Gebhardt also describes a horizontal birth position for noctule bats, with the back facing downwards. The female spreads her hind-legs slightly and folds her tail membrane towards her belly to form a kind of pouch. Young are usually born by pelvic presentation, but head-first births also occur. The baby is caught safely in the pouch formed by the mother's tail membrane. The umbilical cord too can act

(Above left) Part of a nursery roost of Geoffroy's bats (*Myotis emarginatus*) in an attic. A dark-coloured juvenile can be seen in the bottom centre.

(Below left) A five-day-old baby pipistrelle (*Pipistrellus pipistrellus*) attached to its mother's nipple.

A nursery colony of pipistrelles (*Pipistrellus pipistrellus*) packed tightly into a corner of a roof space. The grey-coloured bats are half-grown babies.

as a safety line to prevent the baby falling. Babies that fall off immediately at birth are usually not picked up by their mothers and so perish. The baby's weight at birth is from one-third to one-fifth of the mother's weight, and is lower for species that give birth to two young. The pink, almost completely naked and blind young of pipistrelle bats are hardly bigger than a bee and weigh 1.3–1.5 g.

Immediately after birth the baby climbs up its mother's body and attaches itself firmly to a nipple. The placenta is ejected later and usually eaten. The mother usually bites through the umbilical cord. The young are licked intensively immediately after birth. During this time they utter high-pitched chirping calls which act as contact noises to help mother and baby recognize each other later on.

Mother bats, such as this greater mouse-eared bat (*Myotis myotis*), only carry their babies in flight if they are disturbed or need to change roosts.

Until they become independent, the young are breast fed. The mothers do not take their babies with them when they fly out to hunt. Before leaving the roost the mothers detach them from the nipple by gently pushing them off with their heads and then leave them on their own in the roost. The youngsters left behind often hang close together forming large groups. Nevertheless every mother recognizes its own baby after returning from foraging and only suckles its own young. The young also recognize their mothers. Babies other than their own are rejected by the mother. This recognition is made possible by the contact calls as well as by specific olfactory cues.

If there any disturbance to a roost, mothers will fly off carrying their young. This makes it possible for a whole nursery colony to leave the roost together and fly to a different one. So that the baby can cling well to its mother, the hind-feet and thumbs are already 80% of their final size at the time of birth, whereas the less important forearm is only 30–40% of its final size.

Young bats develop very rapidly. Their eyes open at between three and ten days of age, depending upon species. Even newly-born bats have a coat of sparse, short, hardly pigmented hair. Proper hair growth begins in the course of the first week of life. Even at the age of only a few days they can walk and climb very well at great speed, and are consequently not as helpless as they might seem at first sight. Young vesper bats have a well-developed set of milk teeth, otherwise known as deciduous teeth. Their permanent teeth break through from approximately the tenth day onwards. Young pipistrelle and Nathusius' pipistrelle bats are ready to fly at the age of three weeks, and larger species, such as mouse-eared and noctule bats, are ready to fly after four or five weeks.

When they are four to six weeks old the young are weaned and then have to hunt for insects on their own. After weaning, the mothers move to the mating roost, whereas the youngsters do not leave the nursery roosts until some time later. During this time they are very vulnerable, particularly in bad weather conditions, as they have not yet gained sufficient fat reserves or experience. Mortality among juveniles during this critical phase reaches 80% in some years. However, there is much yearly variation and the average number of bats surviving their first year is estimated at only 30–40% but can be up to 100% in some years. In the following years the survival rate increases and may average over 80%.

The sex ratio at birth is balanced at 1:1. The mortality rate for males is somewhat higher than for females, although this does not mean that females are left unmated because males can have more than one mate.

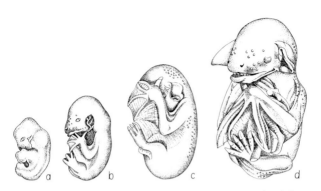

Embryos of a mouse-eared bat at different ages. **a.** crown–rump length 9 mm;
b. crown–rump length 13 mm; **c.** crown–rump length 17 mm; **d.** crown–rump
length not known. Stage **c** shows how the fore-limbs are developing into wings.
The wing is fairly undeveloped at birth, whereas the hind-feet are well developed
for clinging (based on Gebhardt, 1985).

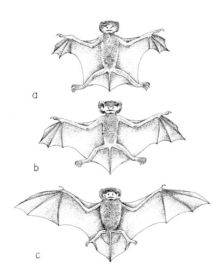

Change in proportions between body and wing size in juvenile noctule bats. The
wings which are underdeveloped until the time of birth grow fully within three
to four weeks. **a.** 1 day old; **b.** 28 days old; **c.** adult about 60 days old (based
on Mohr, 1932).

The social behaviour of bats

Although the behaviour of many species has not yet been studied thoroughly, the basic behaviour patterns of genera or individual species of a family seem to be similar. Many types of behaviour have already been described in earlier chapters, such as flight, echolocation, prey capture and hibernation. Here some other patterns should be mentioned. The basic patterns of behaviour, for example grooming, stretching and sprawling movements, defecation and urination, and wing movements, can be observed in young animals during their first days of life and are therefore innate.

Bats live in groups for most of the year and can therefore be described as highly social mammals. Communal roosting of different species occurs very frequently in the hibernaculum but can also be found in nurseries and other roosts. So far no pecking order has been described for European bats within a group of animals of the same species. Such an order is most likely to occur among males during the mating season. Vesper bats often hang very close together or even on top of each other in their roosts and frequently get in each other's way. The animals then open their mouths wide showing their sharp teeth, utter shrill scolding noises and posture at the troublemaker. This does not usually lead to serious biting or injury. Peace is usually restored after a short while. The facial expressions of 'attacker'and 'defendant' are very similar. The defending animal tends to flatten its ears slightly whilst the attacker pricks its ears up. Bats behave in a similar way if they feel threatened by humans and cannot escape. Larger species when they are roughly handled deliver a strong and painful bite, but smaller species, such as the pipistrelle bat, cannot penetrate the human skin. Generally bats when treated carefully do not attempt to bite.

A special form of defensive behaviour can be observed in pipistrelle and Nathusius' pipistrelle bats and probably other

(Above right) This Nathusius' pipistrelle bat (*Pipistrellus nathusii*) is feigning death, a reflex action in this species. Even if the animal is picked up and held in the hand it continues to lie on its back motionless. The pronounced hair growth on the tail membrane can be seen clearly.

(Below right) Bats groom mainly with the claws of their hind feet. This barbastelle bat (*Barbastella barbastellus*) moves its foot over the wing to the head; during this operation the eyes are closed.

representatives of the pipistrelle genus, and in the noctule bat. If the external threat is not acute, the animal presses itself flat to the ground in a shock position; if it is now touched, however, or even turned on its back, it curls up and allows itself to be handled as though it were dead. This condition is called akinesis and constitutes a feigning death reflex. It can be triggered particularly easily in animals that are still slightly torpid and unable to fly.

As with many animals living in social groups, a sort of 'copy cat' behaviour can be observed with bats. If one animal flies off, grooms itself or investigates the food dish in captivity, it seems to have a stimulating effect on its companions to do the same.

Bats of all species devote a lot of time to body hygiene. Bats regularly groom before leaving the roost and again after hunting. They thoroughly lick their wing membranes, pulling them over their faces like masks during this activity. A secretion from the facial glands keeps the membrane elastic. The bat grooms its fur with the claws of its hind feet, licking and cleaning its claws repeatedly at short intervals. During grooming, the bats hang by only one foot and use the other one for grooming, stretching it underneath or over the wing to reach the fur. Repeated stretching of the wings and even shaking of the whole body occurs. In addition, those parts of the chest and stomach that the bats can reach are licked as well. Like all mammals and birds, bats also yawn.

Adult European vesper bats do not usually groom each others' fur. Even the mothers lick their babies for only a few days, after which the young bats groom themselves. Observations of Mediterranean horseshoe bats have shown that in this species even adult animals lick each others' faces and heads. The animals often hang front to front with their bellies touching, one animal embracing the other with its membranes.

It becomes clear that the innate elements of behaviour are firmly entrenched when a bat is fed on the ground. Since nearly all species catch their prey in flight, they tend to display the same behaviour on the ground, for example they quickly snatch up a mealworm and, sitting down, try to push it into the pouch formed by the tail membrane. Sometimes this results in them rolling over and losing their prey.

Droppings and urine are passed when the bat awakens as well as during and after feeding. All species also do this in flight. One thing that particularly distinguishes the entrance of pipistrelle bat roosts is the droppings stuck to walls, window panes and

Bats' grooming behaviour is innate. The photograph shows a six-day-old pipistrelle bat (*Pipistrellus pipistrellus*) licking its wing membrane.

When urinating, vesper bats arch up the tail. A drop of urine is visible on the penis of this male pipistrelle bat (*Pipistrellus pipistrellus*).

other surfaces beneath them. This can be a source of annoyance to property owners but does reveal the presence of colonies. If vesper bats are hanging up, they turn around so that their head faces upwards, and lift the tail membrane to prevent it from becoming dirty, before passing droppings or urine. Horseshoe bats do not risk soiling themselves since, instead of folding the tail over the abdomen like vesper bats, they fold it over the back when hanging up.

Finally, one aspect of behaviour should be mentioned that can cost the lives of many bats entering buildings in search of roosting sites: before landing, vesper as well as horseshoe bats fly several practice runs towards the selected site before they turn the body by 180° and hang themselves up head-down. These practice flights can even be observed in roosts that are well known to the bats. Horseshoe bats always land hanging up, whereas vesper bats can also perform a sort of belly flop. Sometimes bats will fly repeatedly over a hollow container they have located (vases, glasses, open-top lampshades, open pipes, double-glazed windows) and then let themselves drop into it. This kind of landing can often be observed in pipistrelle bats but also in brown long-eared, Daubenton's and others. If the container has smooth sides and a small diameter the bats can neither climb nor fly out and inevitably die. Roer in Germany reported one such bat trap, a ventilation pipe containing 1180 dead pipistrelle bats and in England one drainpipe similarly contained over 100 dead juvenile bats. These examples show how bats, which are so marvellously adapted to their natural surroundings, can be defeated by the 'creations' of human civilization.

Hibernation – life in suspended animation

In temperate regions, animals are faced with particular problems during the winter months. Special adaptations are required to survive the cold and the shortage of food. Cold-blooded animals (poikilotherms), such as amphibians and reptiles, are largely dependent upon the ambient temperature. Using their own metabolism, they are unable to raise their body temperature significantly above that of their surroundings. They therefore spend the winter torpid, hidden away in frost-free places, until the warm rays of the spring sun rouse them back into life. In contrast, most mammals are homoiotherms, that is they maintain their body temperature at a more or less constant level independent of the temperature of their surroundings. They protect themselves against the winter cold with thick fur or, as in the case of moles, shrews and mice, seek refuge and protection in underground holes in the earth. In each case they must have sufficient food at their disposal, since they would die of cold without a constant supply of energy.

Birds are homoiotherms too. Many species escape the winter by migrating to warmer regions in which they can also find sufficient food. Some of the bats living in the temperate regions also migrate to climatically more suitable areas in the autumn. But even there, winter can catch up with them, depriving them of their basic food by wiping out all insect life. Therefore all European bats, and also some other animals (hedgehogs, marmots and dormice, for example) have evolved a special survival strategy: in the autumn they put on a large reserve of fat which provides them with the energy to sleep through the cold time of the year when there is no food. Bats also have some brown fat reserves which can be found especially between the shoulder blades. This fat accounts for the fact that in autumn a bat's body weight is at least 20–30% higher than in spring. However, unlike cold-blooded animals, bats are not completely at the mercy of the cold. They control their body temperature with a built-in thermostat and can raise their body temperature

up to the normal level without the aid of external energy. Animals with this ability are referred to as heterotherms.

Bats conserve energy even during the warm part of the year by broadly adjusting their body temperature to that of their surroundings when they sleep during the day. The German biologist Eisentraut described this condition as 'diurnal sleep lethargy'. In this torpid phase bats are not able to fly immediately in cool weather, that is when their body temperature is below 20 °C. They have to raise their body temperature above 30 °C before they go out to hunt in the evening. Studies of young mouse-eared bats have shown that during the first two days of life the young animals behave like cold-blooded animals, that is, they cannot actively regulate their body temperature. They are therefore kept warm by their mothers. Only after two or three weeks when their fur is developed do the young bats react fully like true heterotherms.

As the number of cold nights increases in the autumn, the bat's body gradually adjusts to hibernation. They arrive at their hibernaculum from October/November onwards, the exact time depending upon the external temperature as well as on the individual species.

Each species has a particular temperature it prefers for hibernation and the site is chosen accordingly. All bats need a fairly high humidity in their hibernaculum to prevent themselves dehydrating. Often the air is saturated with water vapour with the result that the animals are covered with drops of moisture. Three groups of bats can be distinguished according to their choice of site within the hibernaculum: species of the first group always hang freely on the ceiling by their hindfeet (horseshoe bats); those belonging to the second group can also hang freely from the ceiling or on the wall but often retreat into niches with a more favourable microclimate such as shafts or crevices (examples are the mouse-eared and Daubenton's bat); and species of the third group, such as pipistrelle bats, usually prefer narrow crevices in which they can be in contact with the wall on all sides if possible. There is great variability in the choice of roosting site in the second and third groups; the decisive factor for the eventual choice is probably to do with the possibilities offered by the particular site and especially on the microclimate.

(Above left) Daubenton's bats (*Myotis daubentonii*) like to seek out narrow crevices for hibernation.

(Below left) Many bats show great adaptability when it comes to choosing a place to hibernate. Here a Daubenton's bat has concealed itself in soil between tree roots protruding into an underground mine.

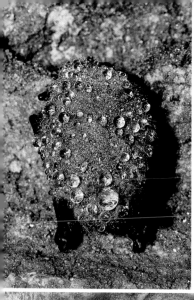

(Left) The high humidity in the hibernaculum often causes the bats, like this Daubenton's bat (*Myotis daubentonii*), to be covered in drops of dew.

(Below) The long extended legs show that this lesser horseshoe bat (*Rhinolophus hipposideros*) is in undisturbed hibernation. It is hanging in a limestone cave. During hibernation bats of this species always wrap their wing membranes around themselves so that their bodies are completely covered.

(Right) Greater mouse-eared bat (*Myotis myotis*) in hibernation. This posture is typical of free-hanging vesper bats. The wing membranes are held at the side of the body and the tail is folded over the abdomen.

During hibernation and diurnal torpor, long-eared bats fold back their large ears and tuck them under their forearms, leaving only the tragus protruding. Pictured here on the left is a grey long-eared bat (*Plecotus austriacus*) and on the right a brown long-eared bat (*Plecotus auritus*)

During hibernation and day torpor, bats assume distinctive body postures: horseshoe bats wrap themselves up in their wing membranes like coats; and long-eared bats fold back their long ears, which contain many blood vessels, and tuck them under their wings. All other vesper bats reduce their body surface area by folding wings and tail membrane tightly against their body.

The fundamental switching of all bodily functions, and especially metabolism, to a much reduced level during hibernation is controlled by complicated hormonal regulatory mechanisms. They cause a reduction in the rate of heartbeat and breathing and in the body temperature.

Studies by the zoologist Kulzer have shown that the heart rate of the mouse-eared bat is up to 880 beats per minute when the bat is active, approximately 250–450 beats per minute when the bat is at rest and only 18–80 beats per minute in deep hibernation. The rate of breathing during the arousal phase is 4–6 breaths per second. This is sharply reduced during hibernation, with breaks of 60–90 minutes occurring between breaths, so that animals appear dead. When active, the body temperature of a mouse-eared bat is around 40 °C, whereas in deep hibernation it is as low as 0 °C. A significant energy saving is achieved by this curtailing of the life processes.

Conserving energy by reducing body temperature is a principle which has been adopted in medicine, but it does not approach the degree of perfection achieved by bats. Since humans are homoiotherms, there is an immediate counter-reaction to external cooling with an immediate compensatory increase in metabolic rate. The use of certain drugs makes it possible to prevent this counter-reaction and body temperatures of 20 °C or less can be achieved. In this state of hypothermia a human's oxygen consumption sinks to 25–30% of normal. This reduction in metabolic rate makes it easier to carry out complicated operations and treat diseases with fevers.

If a bat wakes from hibernation spontaneously or as the result of an arousal stimulus, its breathing and heart beat quickly increase. This leads to an improved oxygen supply to the body and heat production slowly starts. It regains its normal body

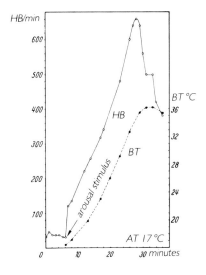

When awakening from a torpid state the increase in rate of heart beat (HB) is ahead of the increase in body temperature (BT). At first the rate of heart beat exceeds the rate which is normal for a bat which is awake and at rest, but after a short time it drops to the normal value (mouse-eared bat, based on Kulzer, 1967). AT = Ambient temperature.

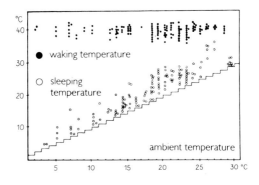

Temperature of a mouse-eared bat when awake and at rest. Measurements carried out on numerous animals show that the temperature during rest is only a few degrees above the ambient temperature (based on Kulzer, 1981).

temperature 30–60 minutes after the start of arousal. The lower the body temperature during hibernation and the lower the animal's energy reserves, the longer the waking process will take. In the first phase of arousal, heat production is achieved largely by burning brown fatty tissue. In the second phase, most of the heat is produced by a clearly visible shivering of the muscles.

When in a state of deep hibernation a bat is helpless and can only carry out very slow reflex reactions. When touched, a bat draws its body up by the legs, opens its mouth and sometimes utters long, high-pitched defensive calls. In such a situation its reflex is to bite and keep its jaws closed for a long time. If a bat is slowly loosened from its surface, it extends its wings and falls spiralling to the ground as though holding on to a parachute. It is very difficult for a bat to turn over if it is lying on its back, whereas it finds it much easier if it can cling to a surface. Only as its body temperature slowly increases does it regain control of all its bodily functions and is able to fly.

During hibernation, arousal can be initiated even by gentle touching, shining of a torch on the animal or taking flash photographs. The animal also wakes up if the temperature in the hibernaculum sinks below the preferred temperature. The animals wake up and look for a site with a more favourable microclimate. Sometimes they even change roost location in winter. However, it is dangerous for bats to stay awake in winter for any length of time since they use up their energy resources too quickly. They then risk either running out of energy for the waking up process in spring or not finding the necessary food.

In contrast to vesper bats, horseshoe bats fold their short tail over the back when at rest. This lesser horseshoe bat (*Rhinolophus hipposideros*) executes a defensive reflex when disturbed in hibernation; it draws its body slowly up by its legs, a sort of chin up.

Loss of heat and thus of energy during hibernation can be prevented by the formation of groups or clusters. This means the animals hang either very close together or even on top of one another like tiles on a roof. This 'social thermoregulation' means that bats at the centre of such a cluster suffer a smaller heat loss than individual animals hanging in isolation. The forming of clusters probably occurs amongst all European species, with the exception of lesser horseshoe bats which always hibernate separately, each hanging at some distance from its neighbours. Some clusters are made up of only a single species, whilst others have been found containing up to five different species. In such clusters one species usually predominates. This type of cluster formation is typical of species such as mouse-eared, noctule and pipistrelle bats.

Bats do not remain asleep for the whole period of hibernation and will wake up several times spontaneously. The duration of the individual periods of sleep depends upon several factors: the

bat's 'inner clock', the temperature in the hibernaculum, the stage of hibernation (beginning, middle or end) and the species concerned. These periods of sleep can last from a few days to one or two months. During the short waking periods the bats fly about in the hibernaculum, passing droppings and urine, and sometimes catching prey or drinking. Mating may even occur in some species, for example Daubenton's and barbastelle bats. Hibernation ends in spring (March/April). The exact time is determined by internal regulatory mechanisms as well as by the outside temperature.

(Left) During hibernation bats are more or less helpless. This greater mouse-eared bat (*Myotis myotis*) which has been laid out on its back has spread out its wings in a reflex reaction and makes slow gripping movements with its feet.

(Right) Large cluster of greater mouse-eared bats (*Myotis myotis*) hanging in a tight group from the ceiling of a concrete tunnel in a mine.

(Below) Mixed cluster made up of Daubenton's bat (*Myotis daubentonii*), a greater mouse-eared (*Myotis myotis*) top right, and barbastelle bats (*Barbastella barbastellus*) centre and left.

Migration to frost-free winter roosts

Bats may migrate long distances between their summer and winter roosts, especially in central and eastern Europe where winters are severe. Species can be divided into those that migrate long distances, those which may migrate short distances and those which are sedentary. Typical representatives of the long-distance migratory species are the noctule and the Nathusius' pipistrelle bat, which generally leave their summer habitats and often travel distances of over 1000 km to their winter roosts further south. Short-distance migrants, for example pond and mouse-eared bats, may travel over 100 km to their winter roosts, whilst sedentary species, such as horseshoe, long-eared and pipistrelle bats, generally do not travel further than 20–50 km. Since the long-distance migrants are seeking milder climates, their migration routes follow a direction that is

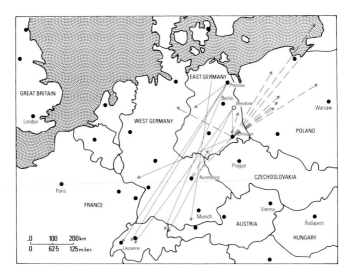

Migration routes and recovery locations of noctule bats (*Nyctalus noctula*) ringed in East and West Germany.
_____ Animals ringed in the summer roost
_ _ _ Animals ringed in the winter roost
(Based on Heise and Schmidt, 1979).

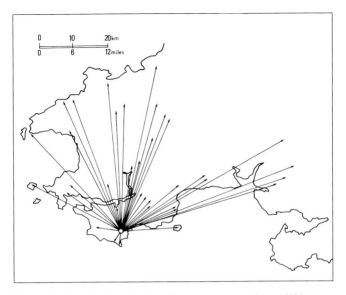

Movements of greater horseshoe bats from a nursery roost in west Wales to hibernation sites. There are also many recorded movements between hibernation roosts (information by Stebbings).

clearly recognizable. Conversely, short-distance migrants and sedentary bats come from all directions to their winter roosts.

Individuals belonging to the latter two groups have frequently been observed to cover much longer distances than is normal for their species. The reasons for this are still largely unknown. Over the whole distribution range of a species, moreover, the migratory behaviour of individual local populations may vary. All populations of a given species living on the northern edge of the distribution range will cover longer distances than the more southerly living, more sedentary populations. Record holders amongst the long-distance migrants are the Nathusius' pipistrelle and noctule bats with migration distances up to 1600 km.

Ringing

The migration routes of bats can only be discovered by marking animals. The German naturalist Eisentraut in 1932 was the first to do large scale ringing in Europe. The C-shaped rings designed in Britain for this purpose by the Mammal Society and issued by them are placed on the forearm so that the ring will slide up and down freely. The rings are made in different sizes and carry an individual number and a brief address. The rings, made of alloy, weigh 0.08–0.14 g and do not impair flight. The ring is initially regarded by the bat as a foreign body and often it will bite at it. In the past this has sometimes caused severe injuries when a weak poor-quality ring has been pressed into the membrane. Longevities of over 30 years and migrations of over 1000 km show that correct ringing does not significantly endanger the animal. However, the question must be asked whether it is still necessary today to ring every animal and every population. Ringing and other marking is now controlled by licencing by the Nature Conservancy Council and the Mammal Society and should only be carried out if it contributes to the solution of scientific questions. The result should directly or indirectly enhance the protection of the animals.

Since the introduction of bat marking in Europe, tens of thousands have been ringed. Unfortunately it is believed that this action directly contributed to the deaths of large numbers of bats. The large number of ringed bats has contributed to answering many questions including:

- the pin-pointing of movements between the individual roost types, particularly between summer and winter sites;

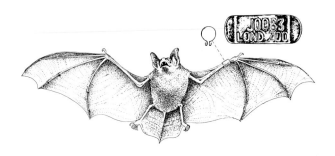

Bat ring. The bat ring is placed on the forearm.

- homing ability;
- faithfulness to roost sites;
- changes in roosting places in the hibernation site and duration of the periods of sleep (marking with colour rings);
- age structure of populations, maximum ages and age to breeding.

Sometimes the catching of bats is necessary for research. Special training has to be given before the following catching methods, described here in outline, can be applied. Some of the methods described are not allowed in Great Britain and some other European countries, so it is important to contact the conservation authority in each country before contemplating any bat research. In the hibernation site it is relatively easy to remove the bats carefully from the roof or from crevices which are not too deep. If the bats are hanging at a considerable height from the ground, helpers should in addition stretch out a safety net below to catch any that may fall.

Catching insectivorous bats in the summer is considerably more difficult. A mist net can be more effective in the tropics and will catch many bats when stretched, not too tightly, across the flight path in front of cave entrances, over small ponds and river courses, and on paths or rides. In order to select the best net position, it is a good idea to observe the bats' flight paths on the previous evening. The net should never be left unsupervised, since the animals could become severely tangled and injure themselves. The larger species also very quickly bite holes in the net.

During emergence from a roost, for example a hollow tree or roof space, bats can be caught with a tightly stretched plastic or gauze bag. Also of proven value is the trap described by Constantine in the USA, which consists of a rectangular frame crossed with vertical 0.1 mm diameter nylon threads spaced 5 cm apart. The lower third of the frame reaches down into a sufficiently deep plastic sack which is also fastened onto the frame. The upper part which resembles a harp is placed in front of the roost exit. The bats fly against the lines of thread and slide down into the plastic collecting bag below from which they cannot escape. Again the trap must be constantly supervised.

What to do if you find a ringed bat.
- If in hibernation, do not disturb or read the ring number.
- If the bat is alive and away from a roost site, read the ring number and address, and release the animal immediately.
- Inform the ringing authority of the ring number, the circumstances in which the animal was found and, if possible, the species and sex of the animal.

Torpid greater horseshoe bat ringed as part of a study into the population dynamics of a colony.

- If the bat is dead, remove the ring and send it in with the other information.
- If possible send a dead animal to a zoological museum as scientific proof (it can be preserved in alcohol).

If the places where the bats are hanging are accessible, the animals can be collected by hand but this must not be done in breeding roosts with dependent young. When collecting in this way, choose cool days, since the bats will be less active. When handling bats it is advisable to wear gloves.

Protect our bats!

European bats have no specialist predators but there are opportunists. Amongst birds it is mainly the tawny owl (*Strix aluco*) and the barn owl (*Tyto alba*) which prey upon bats near the roost site or as they emerge from it. Species which fly in the late afternoon or early dusk may fall prey to falcons. Amongst the small predatory mammals, the weazel (*Mustela nivalis*) and the beech marten (*Martes foina*) have been shown to take bats. Household cats kill many bats and simply leave them lying on the ground, as they do with shrews. It has been observed in countries outside Europe that snakes, for example from the genera *Coluber* and *Elaphe*, have specialized in catching bats at their roost sites or as they fly past.

Ectoparasites (fleas, bugs, bat flies, ticks and mites), which live in the fur and on the flight membranes of all species of bats, may certainly be a considerable nuisance to their hosts, but occur in large numbers only in exceptional cases and mainly on sick or already weakened bats. In Europe, bats are not significant as carriers of diseases which affect man, in contrast to certain rodents. However, since bats, like all mammals, may in exceptional circumstances contract a rabies-like virus infection, gloves should always be worn when handling them, especially those which are grounded or behaving in an abnormal fashion. This particularly applies to the large, powerful species, such as the serotine. No such disease is known from Great Britain despite efforts to find it.

It is not the few natural predators that have been threatening the future of many bat species in the last few decades. Rather it is man with his modern industrial society who is so gravely threatening the existence of these creatures, so much so that certain species of bat have already become extinct in some regions. The greater and lesser horseshoe bats have disappeared from much of their former range in Great Britain and western-central Europe since the 1950's. Populations have disappeared and in many areas there is now virtually no evidence of breeding, with the result that these species may soon die out in these northern areas. The mouse-eared bat is already extinct in Great Britain and, especially in the northern end of its range in continental Europe, there is evidence of a marked decline in numbers. There are populations which are currently only 20% of their original strength and in which many of the breeding colonies have already been extinguished.

There remains hope that, at least at a regional level, fairly large populations may find optimal living conditions and that individuals will reach the age required to ensure the continued existence of the species.

Particular factors which we would like to highlight as being responsible for the drastic decline in bat populations are:

- Reduction or destruction of their sources of food by the use of insecticides and pesticides, and the direct increase in poison levels in bats caused by the eating of insects containing these poisons.
- Destruction of natural landscapes and habitats.
- Destruction of bat roost sites (demolition or modernization of old buildings, hermetic sealing of roof spaces, destruction or complete sealing of underground caves, mines, old vaults and cellars, and felling of hollow trees.
- Use in bat roosts of wood treatment chemicals against woodworm and fungi, such as those used in roof spaces, which are highly poisonous to warm-blooded animals.
- Serious disturbance and killing of bats by people.
- Unfavourable climatic factors (longer cold and wet spells in spring and summer causing increased mortality of juveniles and in animals waking up from hibernation).

All bats in any area are subject to these factors in more or less equal measure. It is noticeable that not all species are affected to the same degree but there is little detailed information. A few populations of Natterer's and brown long-eared bats show hardly any decline. Indeed the numbers of Daubenton's bat in recent years have increased in a few sites in Great Britain and in west and central Europe. Conversely, the cold-resistant barbastelle bat has shown as drastic a decline as that of the warmth-loving mouse-eared bat and the horseshoe bats already mentioned. Even the commonest bat, the pipistrelle, has declined by over 60% in 10 years in Great Britain. The precise reasons for these varied reactions of the different species are not known. It is conceivable that the prey insects of the individual species have been affected differently by insecticides and loss of natural habitats, but lack of results often hampers objective assessment.

All species of bat are protected by law in all European countries. In Great Britain, the Wildlife and Countryside Act (1981) gave protection to bats and their roosts, even if no bats are present. However, if bats are unwanted, or if building repairs or timber treatments are planned, the Nature Conservancy

Council (NCC) should be notified in order that free advice may be given on how to prevent bats being needlessly killed. In some countries bats are included in the *Red Data Book* of species threatened with extinction. Statutory protection alone will not, however, halt the decline! The protection of bats, like the protection of all animal species, must first and foremost be about the protection of habitats. Habitats and roost sites must be preserved.

It is important that hibernation sites be secured against unauthorized visitors. The installation of grills with horizontal bars at the entrances to mines or the inclusion of access slits (50–75 cm wide, 15 cm high) in walled-up entrances to underground rooms allows bats continued and unhindered access to their roost sites. These provisions need to be designed carefully and the NCC has to be notified.

In potential hibernation sites with smooth walls and no cracks or crevices, hanging-up places can be created by fastening hollow building blocks or boards to ceilings and walls (allow a gap of 2–4 cm). It may be necessary to improve the internal microclimate by closing or reducing the size of excessively large access holes or ceiling openings. To preserve summer roosts in roof spaces, entrance holes and gaps must be maintained when making any roof improvements. Ventilation tiles with the filter

Special roof tiles with openings, so-called ventilation tiles, allow the bats access to their roost in the roof space (left). The grilling of openings to caves and mine systems protects hibernation sites from unauthorized access (right).

Checking a bat box. Noctules (*Nyctalus noctula*), Nathusius' pipistrelles (*Pipistrellus nathusii*) and pipistrelles (*P. pipistrellus*) all occur in this mixed beech and conifer forest situated close to a lake.

removed or clay pipes let into gable walls are very suitable for this purpose. Horseshoe bats need a free entrance hole which should measure 200 × 300 mm. It is important that pigeons and jackdaws have no access to the roof space in which the bats are living so entrances for bats need careful designing.

Sometimes the householder is disturbed by the droppings which accumulate under the bats. Here plastic sheets laid out or hung up can be of help. The householder should also know that the bat guano is a valuable fertilizer for flowers and garden!

In known nursery roosts, roof repairs and wood treatment should only be undertaken in the period from October to February. Since wood-treatment agents with chlorinated hydrocarbons (Lindane and PCP) and other chemicals can either kill bats or have a toxic effect on them for months, indeed years, it is advisable to use other chemicals which are safe for warm-blooded animals, for example products with a permethrin base. All the above changes to buildings require prior notification to the NCC.

If bats are living in the external wall of the house or behind fascia boards, these features should if possible be maintained. As a replacement or additional site, bat boards fixed 20–30 mm away from the wall can be attached to a sunny wall.

For woodland bats, the preservation of hollow trees is of vital importance. In recent years the erection of bat boxes as replacement holes has proven very successful. Often the first evidence for the presence of a particular species of bat living in an area has come from bat boxes. Moreover, in some cases completely new colonies have established themselves.

Bats show great adaptability and have used a wide variety of box shape and size made from wood or a wood and concrete mixture. In East Germany the FS 1 box developed by Stratmann has been especially successful. This narrow box is economical

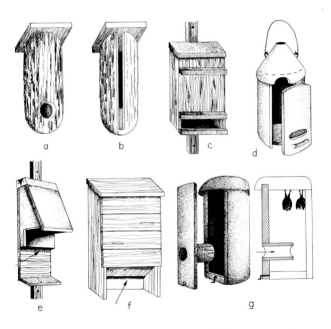

Various types of bat box which are suitable as artificial summer roosts for woodland bats. **a.** Hollowed-out log (corresponds to the upper part of a woodpecker hole). **b.** Hollowed-out log with a slit-shaped entrance. **c.** Wooden and concrete box (model based on Issel). **d.** Wooden and concrete box (model based on Schwegler, 2 FN). **e.** Wooden box (Dutch model). **f.** Wooden box (model based on Stratmann, FS 1). **g.** Wood and concrete pipe box (model based on Nagel).

on materials and easy to construct. It has been occupied by the nursery roosts of Nathusius' and common pipistrelle, brown long-eared, Leisler's, noctule and Brandt's bats. There have also been single records of Daubenton's, Natterer's, serotine and mouse-eared bats. Improvements include covering the box with unsanded roofing felt as suggested by Heisse and wrapping the box in dark painted tinplate (Issel). The higher heat absorption promotes an improved microclimate. Moreover the boxes are largely protected from damage caused by greater spotted woodpeckers. Note also that the boards used in construction must be approximately 25 mm thick. They must be untreated and left rough all over to allow bats to land and crawl about. In Great Britain, the most successful box has been of a simple, easily constructed design by Stebbings (Stebbings and Walsh, 1988).

Bat boxes are fastened, preferably three per tree, at least 5 m above the ground on the sunny side of the trunk. A bat's approach to the box should not be impeded by branches. Since bats frequently change roost sites, five to ten boxes at intervals of 20–25 m should be erected at the edges of paths, rides or clearings. Even if the boxes are not occupied by bats, they often serve as shelter for other animals. Treecreepers, tits and wrens have bred in boxes, and wasps, hornets and slugs have also been known to move in!

If bats are found, whether by chance or by destruction of their roost, they should be released without delay. If an animal appears weak, ill or injured, then it should preferably be taken to a vet.

In the summer, weak or injured bats must first be offered drinking water. Food can be provided in the form of liver or mealworms, the larvae of the beetle *Tenebrio molitor*. Initially it may be necessary to offer the bat only the squeezed contents of mealworms without the chitinous exterior. When feeding and giving water to the bat, it should be held in such a way that the animal is comfortable with the wings held against its body and only the head looks out. With larger species at first leather gloves should be worn to protect the hands from bites until the bat settles down. The mealworm should be coaxed into the bat's mouth until it is accepted. Usually most bats will learn after two to three days to drink water and eat out of a bowl independently. Horseshoe bats, however, can only eat and drink hanging up.

Since mealworms alone do not form a balanced diet, multivitamin preparations and a calcium and mineral salt mixture, such as is used in animal breeding, should be provided once or twice a week. Flies, midges and moths are also a beneficial addition to the diet. A daily supply of food of up to one-third of the bat's body weight must be provided.

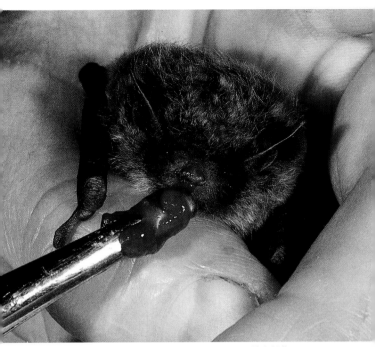

Most captive bats, like this Daubenton's (*Myotis daubentonii*), initially cannot feed independently and must be fed by hand. Raw liver is being given on a paint brush.

The cage in which the bat is kept must allow the bat to hang up and ideally should have a flight area. The bat must be able to exercise daily. The first few days will require a lot of patience. As soon as the bat has recovered well, has regained its normal body weight and flies strongly for a good period of time, it should be released in good weather near to the place where it was originally found.

Which bat is it?

European bats in words and pictures

The following part of this book deals with all European bat species according to a standard format. It does not include descriptions of subspecies or vagrants that have been reported only on extremely rare occasions. The text is laid out as follows:

Body measurements These usually refer to the average size range of a species and are given in millimetres (mm) and grammes (g), with extreme measurements in parentheses. Body measurements of animals of the same species are often lower in the southern part of the species' distribution than in the north (Bergmann's rule). Females are on average larger than males (difference in forearm length c. 1–1.5 mm). Body weight in autumn before the start of hibernation or in late pregnancy females is up to 30% higher than at the end of hibernation or in non-pregnant animals.

Identification Characteristics that are typical to all species of a particular genus are presented in the brief genus descriptions. The description of external features, such as ear shape, is supplemented by colour photographs, and the detailed photographs and illustrations that form part of the identification key. When assessing ear size, it is advisable to consider the great mobility of the ear. The photographs of the ear show it in a largely relaxed shape during a bat's active phase.

The descriptions do not mention characteristics that cannot be established precisely, such as the protrusion of the ear when bent forward over the tip of the nose or the proportion between the length of the thumb and the width of the wrist. Characteristics of the dentition have to be assessed with the aid of a magnifying glass. They can vary to a certain degree and are often more difficult to recognize in old animals with worn-down teeth.

Colour anomalies Known incidences of pigment anomalies, such as partial or complete albinism, are mentioned.

Similar species Species which are easily confused have generally been placed close together in the book. Individual characteristics are referred to under the corresponding species section or in the identification key.

Distribution This information is intended only as a rough guide. Knowledge of distribution is still very sketchy in some cases.

Status and protection All bats are threatened by the destruction of their roosts (in particular the summer and winter roosts), the destruction of insects through the use of pesticides, or poisoning by wood preservatives which are toxic to warm-blooded creatures.

Although insufficient knowledge often makes it difficult to assess the degree to which a species is endangered, such information is included in the *Red Data Books* being produced by most countries and summarized in one volume (Stebbings, 1988). Protection of bats and their roost sites takes priority over research, with the implication that:

- ringing and capture of bats requires a licence;
- some winter or summer roosts, or both, can be visited only for the purpose of carrying out counts or protective measures;
- it is forbidden to remove animals from their sleeping sites or to photograph them;
- animals found dead should be handed over to scientific institutions (museums).

Habitat It must be remembered that individual bat species show great adaptability to different geographical and climatic conditions. The same applies to the temperatures in the hibernacula, the nature of the roost sites and the nursery roosts.

Migration It is of course impossible to make a correct assessment of the migratory behaviour of species that have been insufficiently studied. It must, furthermore, be remembered that even individuals of sedentary species are capable of undertaking long migrations in exceptional cases. The information of record distances covered does not always refer to one season (summer/winter). In some cases ringing and recovery are separated by several years.

Reproduction Dates, such as start and end of hibernation, formation of nurseries and birth of young, vary according to climate. A cold spring for example, may considerably delay the birth of young . Gestation periods vary greatly since they depend upon the climate and are therefore not included.

Maximum age The maximum recorded age attained so far by each species is given; the actual maximum age is probably even higher in some cases. The average age is considerably lower than the maximum life expectancy.

Hunting and diet Lists of prey, which have already been drawn up for some species, have deliberately been omitted. The time of emergence from the roost, the duration of foraging, the height of flight and the type of hunting ground can vary greatly and depend to a large extent on the time of year, weather conditions and type of prey. For most species identification of the bat in flight is impossible. Only the additional use of a bat detector allows any certainty.

Calls It is much more difficult to describe the audible calls of bats than those of birds, thus the information can only serve as a rough guide. Thanks to the development of transportable, electronic ultrasonic detectors it is now possible to convert to audible frequencies the calls that bats emit in flight for purposes of navigation, location of prey, and social communication. Some species of bats can now be recognized in the dark and their flight behaviour studied more easily.

Patient work and observation in the field is still necessary to carry out ecological studies and analysis of aspects, such as the choice of hunting habitat or the repertoire of acoustic signals related to hunting behaviour. Since bat detectors are expensive, advice on the relative merits of the various models should be sought from an expert. Use of a bat detector is not simply a question of pointing the detector at a bat flying by and immediately identifying it.

Studies have shown that, with some practice, many species can be distinguished using criteria such as the form of the signal, its volume, duration, frequency range and rate of repetition. As has been described, horseshoe bats differ from vesper bats in that they emit pure signals of relatively long duration of up to 60 ms (milliseconds), so-called constant-frequency signals (CF signals). Vesper bats, in constrast, produce mainly frequency-modulated signals of short duration (FM signals sweeping between approximately 100 and 12 kHz and 2–20 ms in duration). In some species and in certain situations these FM calls can also include CF components. It is particularly difficult within the vesper bat species to distinguish between the various *Myotis* species, and a distinction between *Myotis mystacinus* and *Myotis brandtii* is virtually impossible. The criteria mentioned are subject to many influences, so that it is advisable to combine acoustic and visual observations.

Of special significance is the recognition of the different phases of the hunting flight: search, approach and catch. During the search phase (regular unhurried, mostly straight flight), the signals are long (2–20 ms), as are the pauses between signals (small species 85 ms, large species up to 300 ms). The approach phase starts as soon as prey has been located. The signals and the pauses in between become shorter. Finally very short signals are emitted during the capture phase (sometimes of only 0.5 ms duration), and the pauses between signals can be reduced to as little as 5 ms.

It is common practice to depict the signal pattern during the search phase in a visual form. This can be done in the form of an oscillogram (wave form, or amplitude, and duration), a sonagram (frequency range and duration of signal), a frequency spectrum [showing the maximum volume in relation to frequency (two-dimensional) as well as duration (three-dimensional)] and impulse repeat rates (number of signals per time unit). Further factors which can affect the nature and pattern of the signal may include: (a) change of habitat in which the bat hunts; (b) change in flight altitude (*Nyctalus noctula* shows a different signal pattern when hunting above the tree tops than when hunting only a few yards above ground level); and (c) whether a bat is hunting in a group or individually. These different factors can sometimes lead to misidentification since often two or more types of signals are used regularly.

The distance over which the calls can be heard depends on the one hand, on the species and the type of signals it is using, and on the other hand on the sensitivity of the detector as well as on the position of the microphone in relation to the approaching animal.

Further illustrations Reference to these is contained in the general part or in the identification key.

The horseshoe bat family (*Rhinolophidae*) Genus: *Rhinolophus* (Lacépéde, 1799)

Approximately 70 species, five of them in Europe. Nose surrounded by leaf-shaped flap of skin consisting of the following parts:

Horseshoe: horseshoe-shaped flap of skin surrounding the nostrils which open at the top of the horseshoe. Distinct notch in the middle of the lower edge of the horseshoe. Upper ends of the horseshoe nearly reach eye level.

Sella: protrudes above the nostril like an upturned hatchet and is surrounded by the horseshoe. Shape and length of upper and lower connecting process important for species identification.

Horizontal fold: runs between sella and lancet.

Lancet: triangular, pointed at top; between the base of the lancet and the upper ends of the horseshoe, there are three cavities on either side, arranged one above the other.

The ears, broad at base and tapering to a point at top, can be moved independently of one another. Tragus absent; antitragus well developed. Eyes small. Wings broad and rounded. Flight

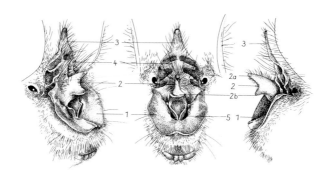

Structure of noseleaf in horseshoe bats (shown here *Rhinolophus euryale*). 1. horseshoe; 2. sella; 2a. upper connecting process; 2b. lower connecting process; 3. lancet; 4. transverse fold below lancet; 5. nostril.

slow, sometimes fluttery like a butterfly, sometimes including short glides, highly manoeuverable. Tail short, fully integrated in flight membrane, folded onto back when at rest. Calcar extends about one third of the length along the tail membrane edge; no post-calcarial lobe.

The females have two mammary glands in the pectoral region and two so-called false nipples located slightly above and to the sides of the genital opening which develop at the first pregnancy (see photograph page 207). The babies cling to these false nipples during the first few days after birth. One young; development of milk teeth only in embryo, not present at birth.

Horseshoe bats always hang freely in their roost, wholly or partially wrapped in their wing membranes, with the baby embraced within the mother's wing membranes during the first days of its life.

In summer, only slightly torpid during the day and can fly off quickly. Often hang by one leg, spinning on longitudinal axis and echolocating. Generally take off by plunging downwards, but can also take off from the ground. Landing occurs after turning axis of the body by 180° so that head points downwards.

Prey is often caught in the wing membrane and can be stored for brief intervals in cheek-pouches. Larger items of prey are consumed at established feeding sites. In captivity, horseshoe bats appear to learn faster than European vesper bats.

Echolocation signals have a long constant-frequency component, with short frequency drop at end (CF/FM signal). To a certain extent frequency can be used to identify a bat since individual species emit signals over a characteristic limited frequency band. Slight frequency variations may occur in a particular species over its geographical distribution range. Echolocation signals are emitted through the nose.

Dental formula $\dfrac{1\ 1\ 2\ 3}{2\ 1\ 3\ 3} = 32$

Lesser horseshoe bat
Rhinolophus hipposideros (Bechstein, 1800)

G Kleine Hufeisennase   **F** Petit rhinolophe fer à cheval

Head–body 37–45 (47) mm
Tail 23–33 mm
Forearm (34) 37–42.5 mm
Ear (13) 15–19 mm
Wingspan 192–254 mm
Condylobasal length 13.4–14.5 mm
Weight (4) 5–9 (10) g

Identification Smallest European horseshoe bat. Delicately built; upper connecting process short and rounded, lower connecting process distinctly longer, pointed in profile. Base of hairs light grey, dorsal side smoky brownish without reddish tint; ventral side grey to grey-white, fur soft and fluffy. Juveniles dark grey. Ears and wing membranes light greyish-brown.

Colour anomalies Flavism (lack of pigmentation with yellow coloration).

Similar species Cannot be confused with other species because of its small size and rounded upper connecting process.

Distribution Most northerly horseshoe bat, occurs up to around 52° latitude. W. Ireland and W. and S.W. United Kingdom, France, Belgium, S. Netherlands, Luxembourg, West Germany (most northerly known location lower Moselle), East Germany (southern central and lower Harz Mountains, N Thuringia, Dresden basin), S. Poland, Czechoslovakia, USSR (Ukraine, Caucasus Mountains).

Status and protection Has become extinct in northern England and north Midlands within the last 50 years. Threatened with extinction in East and West Germany, at risk in Austria; overall serious decline in central Europe, already extinct in northern central Europe. Causes include disturbance and/or destruction of roosts and the use of insecticides; in northern part of range, climatic changes might also contribute to decline. Specific protection of summer and winter roosts necessary! Leave roost entrances (c. 15 × 25 cm) free of obstructions!

Habitat Warmer regions in foothills and highlands, partially wooded areas, areas of limestone. In summer recorded up to 1160 m, in winter up to 2000 m altitude, highest known nursery

The lesser horseshoe bat is one of the smallest of European bats and one of the most sensitive to disturbance.

roost 950 m. House-dwelling in the north and cave-dwelling in the south. In the north summer roosts (nurseries) in warm attics, often near chimneys, in canals and shafts, boiler rooms; in the south in caves and mine tunnels; bat must always be able to fly directly into the roost without obstruction. Hibernacula in caves, mine tunnels, cellars, temperature 6–9 °C, high humidity, always hibernate hanging separately from neighbour, up to 500 animals in the roost. Hibernation from September/October to end of April. Often more males in winter roost than females; they also arrive earlier than females. Hanging height ranges from very close to the ground up to 20 m.

Migration Sedentary species, movement between summer and winter roost 5–10 km, longest movement 153 km.

Reproduction Females are sexually mature in their first year (in Czechoslovakia about 15% of females give birth at one year of age). Mating in autumn, sometimes also in hibernaculum. Animals have been observed to chase each other as preliminary to copulation. The male then hangs himself up behind and over the female. Duration of copulation very brief. Nurseries often shared with other species (greater mouse-eared bat, Geoffroy's bat) but no direct mixing with other species. Move to nurseries from April onwards, about 10–100 females, also males present (up to 20%). Approximately half to two-thirds of females in nursery roost give birth to one young between mid-June and beginning of July. Weight of baby at birth c. 1.8 g, forearm length c. 15–19 mm; covered in fine hair except on abdomen, sensory hairs around the horseshoe. Eyes open after c. 10 days, baby completely independent at 6–7 weeks. Dispersal of nurseries in August to October.

Maximum age 21 years; average age four years.

Hunting and feeding Flight skilful and fairly fast, wing movements almost whirring. Hunts in open woodland and parks, amongst bushes and shrubs. Flies close to the ground, up to 5 m. Picks prey off stones and branches. Catches craneflies, small nocturnal moths, mosquitoes, gnats, beetles and even spiders.

Calls Chirping or scolding.

Echolocation calls Constant-frequency signal of long duration at 105–111 kHz, with short drop in frequency at end. Signal duration c. 20–30 ms. Frequency overlap with Mediterranean horseshoe bat and Mehely's horseshoe bat.

Further illustrations Pages 24, 60, 65, 195, 207.

Lesser horseshoe bat.

Greater horseshoe bat
Rhinolophus ferrumequinum (Schreber, 1774)

G Grosse Hufeisennase   **F** Grand rhinolophe fer à cheval

Head–body (50) 57–71 mm
Tail (30) 35–43 mm
Forearm (50) 54–61 mm
Ear 20–26 mm
Wingspan 350–400 mm
Condylobasal length (19) 20–22 mm
Weight 17–34 g

Identification Largest European horseshoe bat. Upper connecting process short, rounded, lower connecting process pointed in profile. Fur soft, fluffy, base of hairs light grey, dorsal side grey-brown or smoky-grey, more or less reddish tinge. Ventral side grey-white to yellowy-white. Juveniles more ash-grey on dorsal side. Wing membranes and ears light grey-brown.

Wraps itself completely in its wing membranes during hibernation and usually when torpid during the day; like lesser horseshoe bat only slight bending of 3rd to 5th fingers in the joint between the phalanx and the metacarpal and in the joint between 1st and 2nd phalanx. False nipples in females not fully developed until after first birth.

Colour anomalies Not known.

Similar species Cannot be confused with other species because of its size and the blunt upper connecting process.

Distribution Central and southern Europe; in the north up to around 52° latitude, south Wales, south-west England, France, south-east Belgium, Luxembourg, West Germany, south Poland (only one record), south-east Czechoslovakia, in the east as far as Caucasus Mountains. In the south, records for all Balkan and Mediterranean countries.

Status and protection Has disappeared from half of its former range in the United Kingdom and only 1% survive. Also threatened with extinction in northern Europe. Like all horseshoe bats, sensitive to disturbance, therefore specific protection of nurseries and winter roosts required (unobstructed entry holes c. 20 × 30 cm), as is the conservation of basic food sources (no use of insecticides, danger of large beetles being

Greater horseshoe bat.

eliminated by changing cultivation practices in agriculture).
Overall considerable decline in central Europe.

Habitat Warmer regions in areas of open trees and scrub, near
areas of standing or flowing water, areas of limestone, and in
places of human settlement. Mainly house-dwelling in north,
cave-dwelling in south. In mountains usually below 800 m, rarely
up to 2000 m. Summer roosts (nurseries) in the north in warm
attics, church towers; in south mainly in caves and mine tunnels.
Hibernates in caves, mine tunnels, temperature 7–10 °C, rarely
below. Hangs free from ceiling, singly or forms dense clusters
(social thermoregulation). Hibernation from September/
October to April, may be interrupted once or twice per week.
In mild weather it then feeds near the cave entrance.

Migration Sedentary. Distance summer to winter roost usually
20–30 km; longest movement 180 km.

Reproduction Females usually produce their first young when
four years old (England), three years old in south of the

Greater horseshoe bat.

Continent; males become mature at the end of their second year at the earliest.

Mating season from autumn to spring. Nurseries of up to 200 females, males also found in nurseries. In these, females hang together with their young either individually or in clusters. Sometimes they share roosts with Mediterranean horseshoe bats and Geoffroy's bats. Birth from around mid-June and throughout July. One young, opens its eyes at about four days old, is able to fly after three weeks, becomes independent at 7–8 weeks.

Maximum age 30 years; oldest recorded for any European bat.

Hunting and feeding Leaves roost at dusk. Slow, fluttering flight with short glides, usually low (0.3–6 m); little flying activity during wet, windy weather. Hunts in terrain with sparse tree cover, on hillsides, cliff faces, also in gardens. Can locate insects from its resting place and then intercept them. Can pick food off the ground. Catches larger insects (cockchafers, dungbeetles, moths), uses feeding sites. Drinks during low-level flight or hovering. Feeding range of colonies in England 8–16 km.

Calls Relatively deep, chirping or scolding calls.

Echolocation calls Constant-frequency signals of long duration at 77–83 kHz, with short drop in frequency at end (see sonagram on page 210). Duration of signal c. 30–40 ms.

Further illustrations Pages 197, 209.

Mediterranean horseshoe bat
Rhinolophus euryale Blasius, 1853

G Mittelmeerhufeisennase **F** Rhinolophe euryale

Head–body 43–58 mm
Tail 22–30 mm
Forearm 43–51 mm
Ear 18–24 mm
Wingspan 300–320 mm
1st phalanx 4th finger 6.6–8.5 mm
2nd phalanx 4th finger 17.9–19.1 mm
Condylobasal length 16–17.6 mm
Weight 8–17.5 g

Identification Medium-sized. Upper connecting process pointed, slightly bent downwards, distinctly longer than lower connecting process, which looks broadly rounded when seen from below. Lancet tapers off evenly towards the top. Hairless parts of face (horseshoe, lips) light brownish; ears and wing membranes light grey. Fur fluffy, base of hairs light grey. Dorsal side grey-brown, slight reddish or lilac tinge. Ventral side grey-white to yellowish-white; border dorsal/ventral side blurred; often some darker hairs around eyes. Juveniles generally grey. Wings broad, 2nd phalanx of 4th finger more than twice as long as 1st phalanx; at rest 3rd to 5th fingers are slightly bent in the joint between 1st and 2nd phalanx by 180°, therefore bat usually not wrapped up completely in wing membranes (even during hibernation). When active, often hang with bodies in contact, embracing each other with wing membranes and licking each other's faces and heads.

Colour anomalies Albinism.

Similar species Note shape of noseleaf, length of 1st and 2nd phalanx of 4th finger and fur colour compared to Mehely's and Blasius's horseshoe bats; compared to greater and lesser horseshoe bats note difference in size and difference in shape of sella.

Distribution Balkan peninsula and Mediterranean region, also in Sicily, Sardinia and Corsica. Most northerly record in Czechoslovakia (Slovakia), N. Italy, south of France.

Status and protection Decline in numbers in the north of distribution area, particularly in France and Czechoslovakia. Specific protection of roosts and habitat necessary!

Mediterranean horseshoe bat echolocating shortly before flying off. Its mouth is closed as the echolocation calls are emitted through the nostrils.

Habitat Warm, wooded areas in foothills and mountains, prefers limestone areas with numerous caves with water nearby. Summer roosts (nurseries) in caves, in the north sometimes in warm attics (cave-dwelling bat). 50–400 females in nurseries, males also present. Frequently shares roosts with other horseshoe bat species, Geoffroy's bats and long-fingered bats. Winter roost in caves and mine tunnels; temperature around 10 °C. Hangs free from ceiling, sometimes in body contact with others of the same species.

Migration Usually sedentary; longest movement 134 km.

Reproduction No detailed knowledge. One young, weight at birth c. 4 g, able to fly beginning to mid-August. In Bulgaria young are able to fly from mid-July onwards; but pregnant females can be found at the same time.

Maximum age Not known.

Hunting and feeding Leaves roost in late dusk. Hunts low over ground on warm hillsides but also in relatively dense tree cover or scrub areas. Flight slow, fluttering, very agile, able to hover.

Mediterranean horseshoe bat.

Preys on moths and other insects, often eats its prey at feeding sites.

Calls Deep chirping, squeaking or scolding.

Echolocation calls Constant-frequency call at 101–108 kHz with short drop in frequency at end. Signal duration c. 20–30 ms. Overlaps in frequency with lesser horseshoe bat and Mehely's horseshoe bat (see sonagram on page 210).

Further illustrations Pages 86, 197, 199, 207.

Blasius's horseshoe bat
Rhinolophus blasii Peters, 1866

G Blasius Hufeisennase **F** Rhinolophe de Blasius

Head–body (44) 46.5–54 (56) mm
Tail (20) 25–30 mm
Forearm (43.5) 45–48 mm
Ear 16.5–21 mm
Wingspan c. 280 mm
1st phalanx, 4th finger c. 8.2 mm
2nd phalanx, 4th finger c. 14–15 mm
Condylobasal length 15.8–16.7 mm
Weight (10) 12–15 g

Identification Medium-sized. Upper connecting process pointed, straight, not bent downwards, longer than lower connecting process which is narrow and rounded when seen from front. Horizontal fold slightly indented in the middle; lancet tapers off evenly towards the top; horseshoe broad, flesh-coloured, ears and wing membranes light grey. Fur fluffy, base of hairs very light, almost white. Dorsal side grey-brown, sometimes with slight lilac tinge. Ventral side almost white or with slightly yellowish tinge. Border dorsal/ventral side relatively sharp. Dark 'spectacles' around the eyes absent or only hinted at. Wings broad. 2nd phalanx of 4th finger at most twice as long as 1st phalanx.

Colour anomalies Not known.

Similar species Compared to Mediterranean and Mehely's horseshoe bats, note length of 1st and 2nd phalanx of 4th finger and shape of noseleaf; compared to greater and lesser horseshoe bats note differences in size and in shape of sella.

Distribution Only partially known: N.E. Italy, Greece, Yugoslavia, Albania, Bulgaria (Black Sea coast), Sicily, Caucasus Mountains.

Status and protection No detailed knowledge of whether or not it is endangered. Protection of roosts.

Habitat Warm limestone areas with fairly open cover of shrubs and trees. Summer and winter roosts in caves (cave-dwelling bat). No detailed knowledge of hibernation. Hangs freely, no body contact with other bats.

Blasius's horseshoe bat.

Migration Not known, probably sedentary.

Reproduction Nurseries in caves, up to 200 females. One young, no other precise data available.

Maximum age Not known.

Hunting and feeding Probably similar to Mediterranean horseshoe bat.

Echolocation calls Constant-frequency signal at 93–98 kHz, with short drop in frequency at end (see sonagram on page 210). Signal duration c. 40–50 ms.

Further illustrations Page 197.

Mehely's horseshoe bat
Rhinolophus mehelyi Matschie, 1901

G Mehely Hufeisennase **F** Rhinolophe de Mehely

Head–body (49) 55–64 mm
Tail (23) 24–29 (32) mm
Forearm (47) 50–55 mm
Ear 18–23 mm
Wingspan c. 330–340 mm
1st phalanx, 4th finger 7.7 mm
2nd phalanx, 4th finger 19 mm
Condylobasal length (16.1) 16.6–17.5 (18) mm
Weight 10–18 g

Identification   Medium-sized. Upper connecting process relatively blunt in profile, only slightly longer than the lower, the latter being wide and rounded as seen from the front. Lancet narrows sharply in its upper half and tapers off to a thin apex. Horseshoe and lips pale, flesh-coloured, ears and flight membrane grey-brown. Fur relatively thick, base of hairs grey-white. Dorsal side grey-brown. Ventral side almost white; border dorsal/ventral side relatively sharp. Dark spectacles of grey-brown hairs noticeable around the eyes. Wings broad. 2nd phalanx of 4th finger more than double length of 1st phalanx. At rest 3rd to 5th fingers bent by 180° in the joint between 1st and 2nd phalanx. Body thus not completely enveloped.

Colour anomalies   Not known.

Similar species   Compared to Mediterranean horseshoe bat note particular shape of lancet and upper connecting process; compared to Blasius's horseshoe note length of 1st and 2nd phalanx of 4th finger, and nose-leaf appendages. In the case of greater and lesser horseshoe bats note shape of sella and size differences.

Distribution   Only partially known; Spain, Portugal (Mediterranean coast), S. Italy, Sicily, Sardinia, Greece, Yugoslavia, Bulgaria, Romania (Dobrogea) and Caucasus.

Status and protection   Not known how endangered this species is. Protection of roosts and habitats.

Habitat   Cave-dwelling bat. As far as is known, summer and winter roosts in caves, areas of limestone with water nearby, sometimes together with other horseshoes, lesser mouse-eared

Mehely's horseshoe bat. Note the dark 'spectacles' in the region of the eye.

and Schreiber's bats. Hangs free on cave roof. No precise data on hibernation available.

Migration Not known, probably sedentary.

Reproduction No precise data. Nursery roosts once up to 500 animals (Romania). Single young. Young bats in Romania fly second half of July.

Maximum age Not known.

Hunting and feeding Emerges at dusk. Hunts low over ground on warm hillsides, also amongst bushes and trees. Flight slow, very skilful and nimble, partly with short glides. Can take off effortlessly from ground (also feeds on ground?). Preys on moths and other insects.

Calls Relatively deep, loud, short chirping or squeaking.

Echolocation calls Constant-frequency sound at 105–112 kHz,

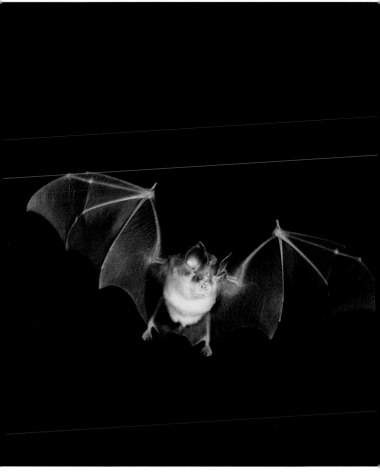

Mehely's horseshoe bat. Due to the short tail length, the tail membrane of horseshoe bats always forms a concave arch during flight; that formed by the tail membranes of vesper bats is pointed or convex (c.f. photograph on page 19).

with short drop in frequency at end. Duration of signal c. 20–30 ms. Overlap in frequency with lesser horseshoe and Mediterranean horseshoe.

Further Illustrations Pages 102, 197, 199

The vesper bat family (*Vespertilionidae*)

Forty genera worldwide with about 320 species, 24 of them in Europe. Nose smooth, without nose appendages; ear with tragus; eyes mostly small; tail completely integrated into tail membrane (except in some species for the last one or two vertebrae); fold their tail onto the belly when at rest. Wings vary from long and narrow to broad and short; when at rest wings are folded and held by the sides of the body. Then the 3rd to 5th fingers are bent inwards by 180° at the joint between the phalanx and the metacarpal (exception: Schreiber's bat). Foot with calcar, sometimes also post-calcarial lobe. Fur colour unobtrusive (black/brown/grey), ventral side lighter than dorsal side. Two mammary glands (exception: parti-coloured bat), no false nipples. Milk teeth present at birth; the number of premolars in the permanent teeth varies from species to species.

Dental formula $\dfrac{2\ 1\ 1\text{–}3\ 3}{3\ 1\ 2\text{–}3\ 3} = 32\text{–}38$

Some species may fly fast and for long periods, sometimes migrating far between summer and winter roosts. Catch prey mostly in the air, but some species also pick prey off the ground or off leaves, branches or other surfaces. Cold-resistant species may occur as far north as the Arctic Circle. Echolocation by means of frequency-modulated (FM) calls; some species can be identified by the specific frequency of their echolocation signals. Emission of calls through the open mouth (exception: long-eared and barbastelle bats, which emit through nose).

Genus: *Myotis* Kaup, 1829

About 90 species, 10 of them found in Europe. Ears longer than they are wide, tragus usually long and lancet-shaped, calcar without post-calcarial lobe, at the most there is a hint of a narrow skin keel. Species vary in size from very large to very small. One pair of mammary glands. Identification difficult if relying on external features. Apart from body size, length and shape of ear, tragus and calcar can help to identify the species.

Dental formula $\dfrac{2\ 1\ 3\ 3}{3\ 1\ 3\ 3} = 38$

Daubenton's bat

Myotis daubentonii (Kuhl, 1819)

G Wasserfledermaus   **F** Vespertilion de Daubenton

Head–body (40) 45–55 (60) mm
Tail (27) 31–44.5 (48) mm
Forearm (33) 35–41.7 (42)mm
Ear 10.5–14.2 mm
Wingspan c. 240–275 mm
Condylobasal length 13.2–14.6 mm
Weight (5) 7–15 g

Identification Medium-sized to small species. Outer edge of ear slightly notched in lower half; ear relatively short, 4–5 transverse folds. Tragus straight, tapering off towards the top, does not reach half the length of the ear. If agitated the bat holds ears folded onto the sides almost at right angles. Fur fluffy, base of hairs dark grey-brown. Dorsal side brown-grey to dark bronze, hair tips often shiny. Ventral side silvery grey, sometimes with a brownish tinge. Border between dorsal and ventral side usually sharp. Nose reddish-brown, ears and wing membranes dark grey-brown. Juveniles greyer, darker. Feet large, long bristles. Calcar reaches approximately two-thirds of the length of the tail membrane, but at three-quarters of the length, an obvious flap in tail membrane edge appears like end of calcar. Lateral membrane starts at base of toes.

Colour anomalies Several recorded instances of albinism.

Similar species Pond bat: larger. Size overlap possible with a number of other *Myotis* species. Long-fingered bat: tail membrane hairy on top, fur greyer, lateral membrane starts above heel. Natterer's bat: calcar bent in an S-shape, hairs along the edge of tail membrane, ears and tragus lighter and longer. Geoffroy's bat: fur usually strikingly reddish-brown, outer edge of ear with distinct notching. Bechstein's bat: distinctly longer ears. Brandt's bat: tragus long, extends beyond notching of back edge of ear, calcar reaches a maximum of half of length of tail membrane, at three-quarters of the length, no flap on tail membrane edge.

Distribution Nearly all of Europe, up to 63° N. Absent only from northern Scandinavia and in the south in the Balkan states (Romania, Bulgaria, Greece and Albania).

104

Daubenton's bat.

Status and protection Moderately common throughout the United Kingdom up to N. Scotland. Endangered in West Germany and Austria, locally endangered in East Germany. Observations in hibernacula in some Mediterranean countries suggest a fairly clear population increase. Causes might be found in their mode of hunting and their diet (no insecticides are used above water surfaces). They are occasionally caught by anglers (hook through mouth or wing). Protection by conservation of roosts (tree holes) and habitats!

Habitat Predominantly in flat countryside, woodlands, parks, usually near water; woodland bat. In summer at 750 m above sea level, in winter recorded up to 1400 m. Summer roosts (nurseries) in tree holes, with circular or slit-shaped entrance holes sometimes less than 1 m above the ground; also in attics. Individual animals and small groups of males often found in cracks under bridges, in walls, rarely in bat boxes. Winter roosts in caves, mine tunnels, bunkers, cellars, old wells. Temperature 3–6 (8) °C, temporarily down to −2 °C; high humidity. Usually squeezed into crevices, but also in large clusters hanging free from the wall, sometimes up to 100 animals arranged like

The open mouth (echolocating) and the lifted left wing indicate that this Daubenton's bat is about to fly off.

roof slates next to and on top of each other.

Has also been found as deep as 60 cm below stones on the cave floor. Several thousand animals in large hibernacula. Hibernation from end September/mid-October to end March/April. Females appear in hibernaculum before males; invasion-like occupation of their normal winter roosts has been observed in August.

Migration Short-distance migrant, mostly under 100 km; descend on hibernacula from all directions. Longest movement 240 km.

Reproduction Some females probably sexually mature in their first year. Mating season from September until spring, often mating in hibernaculum. Nurseries are occupied from around May onwards, 20–50 females, rarely up to 200. During this time males live together in groups of up to 20. Individual males may also be found in nurseries.

Birth of young from second half of June and in July. One young. Dorsal side, ears and wing membranes at birth are grey-brown, ventral side is pink. Already covered in very thin, short hair on dorsal side, sensory hairs on tail. Weight at birth around 2.3 g, forearm 14.9 mm. At ten days: weight 4.3 g, forearm 24.1 mm. At 21 days: weight 5.5 g, forearm 32.7 mm. Eyes open from 8th to 10th day, complete hair cover from 21st day, hair growth complete at 31–55 days. Adult dentition complete around 31st day. Able to fly at the beginning of the third week; nurseries disperse in August.

Maximum age 20 years. Average age 4–4.5 years.

Hunting and feeding Leaves roost at twilight. Flight fast, agile; wingbeat fast, sometimes even whirring. Hunts frequently only 5–20 cm above the water surface but also around trees at heights of up to 5 m; during hunting takes a rest by hanging on branches or walls. Preys on small flying insects (for example, gnats, mosquitoes and moths), eats during flight. Hunting areas in most cases only 2–5 km from roost.

Calls Chirping calls during flight, in defence shrill scolding, long shrill calls if disturbed in hibernation.

Echolocation calls (search flight) FM signals at 69–25 kHz (78–32 kHz). Duration 3–4 (6) ms. The call shows a sine wave amplitude modulation (c. 10 maxima); highest intensity at 45 kHz; signal sequence every (35–) 75 ms; about 13 (–28) signals per second. Range 20–40 m (see sonagram on page 211).

Further illustrations Pages 22, 43, 58, 60, 67, 201, 205.

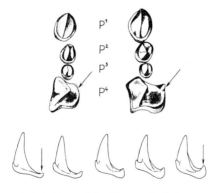

Variation of morphological types of the 4th premolar in the upper jaw (P^4) in a number of Daubenton's bats (based on Hanak, 1983/84).

Long-fingered bat
Myotis capaccinii (Bonaparte, 1837)

G Langfussfledermaus **F** Vespertilion de Capaccini

Head–body (43) 47–53 mm
Tail 35–42 mm
Forearm (37) 38–44 mm
Ear 14–16 mm
Wingspan 230–260 mm
Condylobasal length 13.9–14.8 mm
Foot 11–13 mm
Weight 6–15 g

Identification Medium-sized. Ears of medium length, narrow, outer edge to point slightly notched, five horizontal folds, tragus pointed, reaches half ear length, inner edge convex, outer edge concave and slightly serrated. Base of hairs dark grey. Dorsal side light smokey grey, partly tinged with light yellow. Ventral side light grey; border dorsal/ventral side blurred. Nose rusty brown, ears and flight membranes grey-brown. Feet noticeably big with long bristles, wing membrane above and below covered with thick downy brown hair from the legs down to around the middle, hairs in the calcar region extend out over the edge of the tail membrane; Calcar straight, reaches about one-third of the tail membrane; two-thirds to three-quarters of the length of the calcar a break appears which looks like end of calcar. Lateral membrane wide, starts 3–5 mm above heel on the lower leg. Nostrils more clearly prominent than in other European *Myotis* species.

Colour anomalies Not known.

Similar species Daubenton's, Natterer's, pond, Bechstein's and Geoffroy's bats – none of these has hair on tail membrane. For further features see Daubenton's bat and page 185 onwards.

Distribution European Mediterranean area and Balkan countries; only partially known; northern extremity of distribution in Spain, south of France, Italy, Switzerland, (south Tessin), Yugoslavia, Bulgaria, Greece. Apparently only slight overlap in range with Daubenton's bat.

Status and protection How endangered this species is cannot be assessed. Protection of caves (summer and winter roosts).

Habitat Limestone areas, wooded or scrubby terrain near water. Summer and winter roosts in caves (cave-dwelling bat), in hibernaculum often in crevices.

Migration Not known; sedentary or short-distance migrant?

Reproduction Knowledge incomplete. Nursery roosts in caves with up to 500 females in clusters on cave roof. Birth mid- to end June. One young. Juveniles fly from 2nd third of July.

Maximum age Not known.

Hunting and feeding Emerges in late dusk. In flight resembles Daubenton's. Often hunts over water. Preys on flying insects.

Calls Audible calls shrill scolding, similar to Daubenton's bat.

Further illustrations Page 205.

Long-fingered bat.

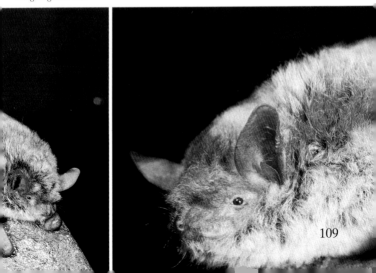

109

Pond bat
Myotis dasycneme (Boie, 1825)

G Teichfledermaus   **F** Vespertilion des marais

Head–body 57–67 (68) mm
Tail (39) 46–51 (53) mm
Forearm (41) 43–49.2 mm
Ear (14.9) 16–19 mm
Wingspan 200–320 mm
Condylobasal length 15.7–17.4 mm
Weight (11) 14–20 (23) g

Identification Medium-sized. Outer ear edge without any obvious indentation, five horizontal folds, tragus visibly shorter than half ear-length, very short for *Myotis* species, tapers off only slightly at top, rounded tip, slightly bent inwards. Fur thick, base of hairs black-brown. Dorsal side brownish or pale grey-brown with silky sheen. Ventral side white-grey to yellowish-grey, fairly sharply defined border with dorsal side. Juveniles overall darker coloured. Nose short, red-brown, ears and flight membranes grey-brown. Wings long and broad, lateral membrane starts at heel; feet large with long bristles. Fine white hairs along lower part of leg on underside of tail membrane. Hairs extend over end of tail membrane at calcar. Calcar straight; reaches about one-third length of tail membrane, three-quarters of way along is an obvious flap which appears like end of calcar.

Colour anomalies None known.

Similar species The very similarly coloured Daubenton's bat is smaller, note also tail membrane and tragus. Long-fingered bat has hair on upper side of tail membrane, for other details see identification key.

Distribution In central and east Europe in a broad band at 48–60° N, from N.E. France across Belgium, Holland, Denmark, southern Sweden, Poland to the Baltic Soviet Republics. In the south across Czechoslovakia, Hungary to the Ukraine and the Byelorussian Soviet Republic. In West and East Germany generally only isolated winter records and also a few summer records in East Germany. Centres of distribution with nursery roosts occur in the Netherlands (Friesland and N. Holland), Denmark (Jutland) and Lithuania.

Pond bat.

Status and protection World endangered species with large decline in numbers in west of range. Many nursery sites have been lost in the Netherlands. Specific protection of nursery and hibernation roosts required in the few known centres of distribution; habitat protection. Care needed with wood treatment!

Habitat In summer areas of water with meadows and woods in lowland regions, in winter also in foothills of mountains; records up to 1000 m above sea level. Winter roosts generally not more than 300 m above sea level. Summer roosts (nursery roosts) mostly in roof spaces or church towers, often large groups in the darker parts of the ridge. Individual animals also in hollow trees.

Hibernation roosts in natural caves, mines, cellars, bunkers; temperature 0.5 –7.5 °C. Hibernation from October to mid-March/April. May be found either wedged in crevices or hanging from ceiling or on walls. In winter sites, up to several hundred animals, when small clusters may occur.

Migration Occasional migrant, migrations from more northern summer roosts to the more southerly hibernacula, generally over 100 km. Furthest recorded journey 330 km.

Reproduction Sexual maturity of females probably in second year. Mating season from end of August, pairing also occurring in hibernaculum. Nursery roosts are occupied in May, with 40–400 females, but rarely any males, which at this time live singly or in small groups distributed over a wide area. The females may change nursery roosts from year to year. Births from mid-June, one young, independent from around mid-July; dispersal of nursery roosts in August.

Maximum age 19 years.

Hunting and feeding Emergence in late dusk. May be two foraging periods, in evening and early morning. Hunts over water, over meadows and along woodland edges. Flight rapid, skilful, over water often only 5–10 cm above surface. Preys on gnats, mosquitoes, moths and takes insects off water surface.

Echolocation calls (searching flight) FM signals from 60 to 24 kHz, sometimes ending in CF signal. Duration 5–8 ms; highest pulse intensity 36–40 kHz. Call sequence every 115 (90–130) ms (approximately 8–10 signals per second); signal range 5–20 m (see sonagram page 209).

Further pictures Pages 201, 205.

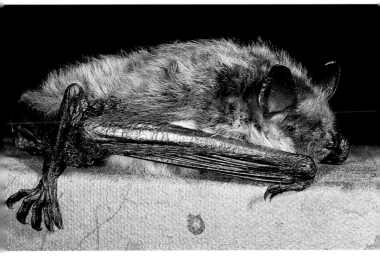

Pond bat. Note the large feet.

Brandt's bat
Myotis brandtii (Eversmann, 1845)

G Grosse Bartfledermaus   **F** Vespertilion de Brandt

Head–body 39–51 mm
Tail 32–44 mm
Forearm 31–39 mm
Ear 13–15.5 (17) mm
Wingspan 190–240 mm
Condylobasal length 13.1–14.4 mm
Weight 4.3–9.5 g

First discovered in Europe in 1958 by Topal.

Identification Small. Edge of outer ear with clear indentation, which is below tip of long pointed tragus, 4–5 transverse folds. Fur relatively long, base of hairs dark grey-brown. Dorsal side light brown, mostly with gold sheen. Ventral side light grey, partly yellowish tinge. Nose, ears and flight membranes medium to light brown, base of tragus and inner edge of ear obviously lighter. Wings relatively narrow, lateral flight membrane starts at base of toes. Feet small. Calcar shorter than half length of tail membrane; usually narrow keel of skin on outer edge. Penis on adult male obviously club-shaped at end. Cusp on P^3 higher or equally high as P^2, P_2 not significantly smaller than P_1. Juveniles strongly resemble whiskered bat; dorsal side dark black-brown to grey-brown, nose and ears black-brown. Lively behaviour, but not so temperamental as whiskered bat.

Colour anomalies Unknown.

Similar species Whiskered bat: penis not club-shaped at end, colour of ears and nose black-brown, base of tragus and inner edge of ear not lighter. Daubenton's bat: note shorter tragus, length and shape of calcar and tail membrane. Geoffroy's bat: dorsal side mostly red-brown, never with golden sheen, note shape of ear and tragus length.

Distribution Only partially known, since previously was not distinguished from the whiskered bat. England and southern Scotland, extreme N.E France, Belgium, Holland, West and East Germany, Scandinavia up to 64° N., Poland, Baltic Republics. In the south, reaches Switzerland, Austria, Hungary and Bulgaria; widely distributed in Asia.

113

Brandt's bat

Status and protection Widespread over England and Wales, and has been found in S. Scotland. Extremely endangered in West Germany, endangered in Austria, rare in East Germany. The erection of bat boxes in suitable habitats is recommended.

Habitat Woodland bat, compared to whiskered bat more frequently found in woodland and areas of water, less often in human settlements. In winter recorded up to 1730 m above sea level, highest nursery roost 1270 m (Switzerland). Summer roosts (nursery roosts) in narrow crevices in the roof timbers of buildings, behind roof boarding, in holes in beams, also in bat boxes. Hibernation sites in caves, tunnels and mine workings, cellars; temperature (0 °C) 3–4 °C (7.5 °C). In roost often found with whiskered bat, mostly hanging freely on wall or ceiling, rarely in cracks. Also in clusters with Daubenton's bats. Hibernation from around October to March/April.

Migration Occasional migrant. Furthest movement 230 km.

Reproduction Age of sexual maturity in females not known, probably in second year. Mating in autumn and in hibernaculum. Nursery roosts are occupied in May, around 20–60 females, mixed nursery roosts with Nathusius' pipistrelle bats in boxes have been recorded. Births mid-June to mid-July. One young. Newly born dark grey on dorsal side, ventral side lighter; ears limp; dorsal side covered with hardly visible fine hairs. At 10 days: weight 3 g, forearm 20.3 mm. At 22 days: weight 4.5 g, forearm 32.2 mm, wingspan 200 mm. Eyes open from 3rd day, ears erect between 5th and 9th day. Can fly at 3–4 weeks. Penis of juvenile males not yet club-shaped.

Maximum age 19 years 8 months.

Hunting and feeding Emergence in early dusk. Hunts at low to medium height in woodland which is not too dense, often over water. Flight rapid and skilful with quick turns, not so skilful in confined spaces as whiskered bat. Range of diet not known exactly, probably small moths and other flying insects.

Calls High chirping and scolding when disturbed. Young in nursery roost make high twittering noise (isolation calls).

Echolocation calls (searching flight) Same signal pattern as whiskered bat.

Further illustrations Pages 40, 117, 119, 201, 204, 209.

Brandt's bat with nearly adult grey juvenile. The colour difference between the adult and juvenile is particularly marked in this species.

Whiskered bat
Myotis mystacinus (Kuhl, 1819)

G Kleine Bartfledermaus   **F** Vespertilion à moustaches

Head–body 35–48 mm
Tail 30–43 mm
Forearm (31) 32–36 (37.7) mm
Ear 12–17 mm
Wingspan 190–225 mm
Condylobasal length 12.3–13.3 (13.6) mm
Weight (3) 4–8 g

Identification Smallest European *Myotis* species. Outer edge of ear with clear notching, which is below the end of the long tragus, 4–5 transverse folds. Nose, ears and wing membranes black-brown, base of tragus and inner edge of ear not light like that of Brandt's bat. Fur long, somewhat shaggy, base of hair dark grey. Colouring of dorsal side strongly varied – dark nut-brown or dark grey-brown, or more rarely light brown; generally darker than Brandt's bat. Ventral side dark to light grey. Juveniles darker, base of hair black, dorsal side dark grey-brown. Wing membranes relatively narrow, start of lateral membrane on base of toes. Feet small. Calcar shorter than half tail membrane, and mostly has narrow keel. Penis thin, not club-shaped at end. Cusps on P^3 lower than on P^2, P_2 obviously smaller than P_1. It is the liveliest in temperament of the *Myotis* species.

Colour anomalies Albinism.

Similar species Brandt's bat: see equivalent section on this species. Pipistrelle bat: different ear and tragus shape, calcar with post-calcarial lobe.

Distribution Throughout Europe except central and northern Scotland and northern Scandinavia, reaches 65° N. Main concentration of distribution is in Central Europe. In south occurs in Balkans and Mediterranean area; few records from N. Spain.

Status and protection Widespread over England and Wales, but rare in the east. Most threatened by chemical remedial timber treatments. Specific protection of known nursery roosts and hibernacula needed and protection of habitat.

Habitat Not as obviously associated with woodland and water

Whiskered bat (left) and Brandt's bat (right). The difference in colour between adults of the two species is not always so clear-cut.

as Brandt's bat, more in parks, gardens, villages, more a house-dwelling than woodland bat. In south-east Europe also in limestone areas. In summer, up to 1920 m above sea level (Col de Bretolet, Alps), in winter up to 1800 m (Tatra Mountains, Poland). Summer roosts (nursery roosts) in lofts and in narrow crevices accessible from outside, between timbers and masonry, behind weather boarding and in bat boxes. Hibernates in caves, mine tunnels, cellars; temperature 2–8 °C. Mostly hanging free on the wall or ceiling, but also wedged in cracks. Hibernacula with over 100 animals are very rare. Males often predominate in hibernacula. Hibernates from October to March.

Migration Mainly sedentary but may also be an occasional migrant. Furthest recorded distance 240 km.

Reproduction Females may mate in their first year. Mating takes place from autumn to spring, including period of hibernation. Nursery roosts are occupied from around May, 20–70 females; the males live singly at this time. Births from mid-June. One young. Dispersal of nurseries at end of August.

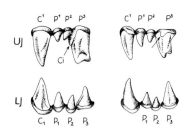

Brandt's bat (left) and whiskered bat (right). Important teeth for identification of species in upper jaw (UJ) and lower jaw (LJ). Rows of teeth viewed from inside (C canine and P premolar). Note the length of the cusp Ci (cingulum cusp) on P^3 in relation to P^2.

Maximum age 19 years. Average age four years.

Hunting and feeding Emergence in early dusk. Forages at 1.5–6 m above ground in parks, gardens, and over flowing water, as well as above meadows or in woodland. Hangs on branches to rest. Flight rapid, agile and weaving. In spring and autumn occasionally hunts in daylight. Prey insects: midges, mayflies, small dragonflies, beetles and moths.

Calls Long, high-pitched scolding or twittering if disturbed.

Echolocation calls (searching flight) FM signals from 75–32 kHz (see sonagram on page 211). Duration: 2.5–3 ms; highest pulse intensity 40–50 kHz. Sequence of calls every 90–100 ms (around 10–11 signals per second). Range 5–20 m.

Further illustrations Pages 135, 201, 209.

Whiskered bat.

Geoffroy's bat
Myotis emarginatus (Geoffroy, 1806)

G Wimperfledermaus   **F** Vespertilion à oreilles échancrées

Head–body 41–53 mm
Tail 38–46 (48) mm
Forearm 36–41 (42) mm
Ear 14–17 mm
Wingspan 220–245 mm
Condylobasal length 14–15.7 mm
Weight (6) 7–15 g

Identification Medium-sized. Ear of medium length, outer edge with distinct, almost perpendicular, notches in upper third, 6–7 transverse folds, tragus lancet-shaped, more or less distinct fine notches along outer edge, almost reaches height of notches on outer edge of ear. Fur long, fluffy, of woolly appearance, hairs on dorsal side of three colours: base grey, middle straw-yellow, tips strikingly rusty-brown to foxy-red. Ventral side yellowish-grey. Juveniles considerably darker, smokey-grey to brown-grey, without reddish tinge. Nose red-brown, ears and wing membranes darker grey-brown. Wings relatively broad, lateral membranes start at base of toes, feet small. Calcar straight, reaches about half length of the tail membrane, free edge of tail membrane with sparse, short, straight, soft hairs ('eyelashes').

Colour anomalies Not known.

Similar species Natterer's bat: colour greyer, calcar S-shaped, free edge of tail membranes densely covered with strong, bent bristles. Brandt's bat: tragus higher than notches on hind edge of ear, hairs on dorsal side not three-coloured. Daubenton's bat and Bechstein's bat: see identification key.

Distribution Central and southern Europe, northern Portugal, Spain, France, Belgium, S. Netherlands; rare in S. West Germany (Bavaria); more common in Czechoslovakia, Italy and Balkan Peninsula.

Status and protection Endangered and almost extinct in northern areas including West Germany and Austria. Specific protection of roosts necessary; care with wood treatment measures essential!

Habitat Prefers warmth, mainly house-dwelling in the north, cave-dwelling in the south; in lowland and lower mountain

Geoffroy's bat.

regions, in limestone areas as well as in populated areas with parks, gardens and water; in mountains up to 1000 m. Summer roosts (nurseries) in warm attics (36–40 °C). Hang free from rafters or top ridge, in southern Europe usually in caves and mine tunnels. Winter roosts in caves, mine tunnels and cellars; temperature 6–9 °C rarely below. Mostly hanging singly from roof or on wall, rarely in small clusters or in crevices. Hibernation from October to March/April.

Migration Predominantly sedentary, movements usually under 40 km, longest 106 km.

Reproduction The females can be mated in their first year, but giving birth at the end of their first year has not yet been proven. Mating season starts in autumn; no information available on matings in hibernacula. Nurseries formed around May, often in roost shared with horseshoe bats; nursery size ranges from 20–200 females (Czechoslovakia) to 500–1000 females (France, Balkan states). Births mid-/end of June to beginning of July. One young, able to fly at about four weeks. Dispersal of nurseries in September.

Geoffroy's bat.

Maximum age 16 years. Average age 3.5 years.

Hunting and feeding Emerge in early dusk. Hunt at 1–5 m above ground. Flight manoeuverable, hunts also above water. Preys mainly on spiders but will also catch diptera, such as gnats, also moths and caterpillars. Prey is also picked off branches or off the ground.

Calls In nurseries loud, shrill scolding.

Further illustrations Pages 46, 122, 199, 203.

Natterer's bat
Myotis nattereri (Kuhl, 1818)

G Fransenfledermaus **F** Vespertilion de Natterer

Head–body (40) 42–50 (55) mm
Tail 38–47 (49) mm
Forearm 36–43 (46) mm
Ear 14–18 (20) mm
Wingspan 245–300 mm
Condylobasal length 14–15.6 mm
Weight 5–12 g

Identification Medium-sized. Ear relatively long, outer edge with five transverse folds and distinct notch which is exceeded in length by long lancet-shaped tragus; tragus longer than half length of ear. Nose relatively long, upper lip with hint of beard formed by longer hairs. Fur long, fluffy, base of hairs dark grey. Dorsal side lighter grey, only slight brownish tinge. Ventral side light white-grey, distinct border between dorsal and ventral side. Nose light flesh-coloured, ears and wing membranes light grey-brown, tragus light yellowish-grey, darker towards tip. Wing membranes broad, starting at base of toes. Calcar reaches about half the length of the tail membrane, S-shaped bend in calcar, free edge of tail membrane wrinkled, densely covered with two rows of stiff, downward-curving bristles ('fringes').

Colour anomalies Not known.

Similar species Long-fingered, Daubenton's, pond, Geoffroy's and Bechstein's bats, see relevant species descriptions and identification key. None of these species has an S-shaped calcar.

Distribution Nearly throughout Europe, in Ireland, United Kingdom, Denmark, southern Sweden, Estonia and the Mediterranean countries; absent from the Netherlands, Romania and Sardinia.

Status and protection Widespread throughout the United Kingdom to N. Scotland. Highly endangered in West Germany. Threatened by loss of roosts, especially by chemical remedial timber treatment, felling of hollow trees and destruction of hibernacula.

Habitat Predominantly a woodland bat, forests and parks with areas of water and marsh, also in areas of human population; recorded in summer up to 1920 m (Col de Bretolet, Alps), in

123

winter up to 800 m. Summer roosts (nurseries) in tree holes and bat boxes in woodlands but also in cracks on or in buildings (in roof spaces, more rarely in top ridge). Nurseries and individual animals in cracks under bridges. Winter roosts in mine tunnels, caves, cellars; temperature 2.5–8 °C, for a short period even as low as 0.5 °C. High humidity. Usually squeezed in narrow cracks, sometimes lying on its back; may also be found in scree on ground or hanging free from roof or wall. Occasionally in small clusters, then often mixed with Daubenton's bats. One large cluster of more than 160 bats known from England. Hibernation from October to April, usually enters hibernaculum later than Daubenton's bat.

Migration Sedentary species. Longest movement 90 km.

Reproduction No precise information available concerning the start of sexual maturity. Mating from autumn to spring. Nurseries are occupied from April/May, 20–80 females, or more, sometimes individual males as well. Births take place from

Natterer's bat.

124

Hibernating Natterer's bats. The relatively long ears jutting out beyond the nose tip can be seen clearly.

mid-June through July. One young. Nursery roosts may be changed very frequently (up to once or twice per week).

Maximum age 20 years.

Hunting and feeding Emerges in late dusk. Flight low (1–6 m above ground level), wing beat slow, sometimes whirring, highly manoeuverable in confined spaces, also able to hover for short periods. Hunts in woodland, also above water; usually throughout the night. Prey consists mainly of diurnal flies and diptera which are picked off leaves, branches and other surfaces which serve as their resting places at night.

Calls Chirping or squeaking, deeper than Daubenton's bat; if alarmed may emit deep humming noise; high, shrill calls in flight.

Echolocation calls (search flight) FM signals at 78–35 kHz; duration 2 ms (see sonagram on page 211). Highest pulse intensity at 50 kHz. Signal sequence every 70–90 ms (11–14 signals per second); range: 5–20 m. The calls are not as loud as those emitted by *Myotis mystacinus*.

Further illustrations Pages 19, 24, 201, 205, 207.

Bechstein's bat
Myotis bechsteinii (Kuhl, 1818)

G Bechsteinfledermaus   **F** Vespertilion de Bechstein

Head–body 45–55 mm
Tail (34) 41–45 (47) mm
Forearm 38–47 mm
Ear (21) 23–26 mm
Wingspan 250–300 mm
Condylobasal length 16–16.8 mm
Weight 7–14 g

Identification Medium-sized. Ears strikingly long and fairly broad, extend beyond nose when folded forwards, outer ear edge with nine transverse folds; tragus long, lancet-shaped, reaching roughly halfway up the ear. Fur relatively long, base of hairs dark grey-brown. Dorsal side pale-brown to reddish-brown. Ventral side light grey. Juveniles light to ash grey. Nose reddish brown, ears and wing membranes light grey-brown. Wings broad and short, lateral membrane starts at base of toes; feet small. Calcar straight, reaching about one-third to one-half of length of tail membrane, last tail vertebra free.

Colour anomalies Partial albinism (white tips on both wings).

Similar species Long-eared bats: longer ears joined at base at the front. All other *Myotis* species of similar size have considerably shorter ears.

Distribution Apparently only local distribution and not common in any area. Southern England, France, Belgium, Netherlands, West Germany, East Germany, S. Sweden, S. Poland and Mediterranean countries, but not in Albania, Greece or Romania.

Status and protection In United Kingdom, occurs mainly in Dorset, Wiltshire and Hampshire. Very rare everywhere and recognized as endangered in West Germany and Austria. Since it occurs in only small numbers anywhere, specific protection of known nursery roosts important; erection of bat boxes.

Habitat Woodland bat; mainly damp mixed woodland but also in pinewoods, parks and gardens in lowland and highland regions. In summer, up to 800 m, in winter up to 1160 m. Summer roosts (nurseries) in tree holes and bat boxes (not flat boxes), less common in buildings, where free-hanging.

Bechstein's bat.

Individual animals also in rock caves. Winter roosts in cellars, mine tunnels, caves and in tree holes. Temperature 3–7 °C, high humidity. Often hangs free from roof or wall, or more rarely squeezed in narrow crevices; mostly individual animals, not clusters. Ears held straight even during hibernation. Hibernation from October until March/April.

Migration Apparently sedentary. Longest movement 35 km.

Reproduction Age at which sexually mature not known. Mating season from autumn to spring; occupation of nursery roosts from end of April/May (changed frequently), 10–30 females. Births end of June to beginning of July. One young, able to fly beginning or mid-August; dispersal of nurseries end of August. In summer males live on their own.

Maximum age 21 years.

Hunting and feeding Emerges only after nightfall, fluttering flight, very agile even in very confined space. Hunts low (1–5 m), may also pick prey off twigs or off the ground. Catches moths, mosquitoes and beetles.

Calls Hollow humming or chirping when threatened, no audible calls in flight.

Partially albino Bechstein's bat with white wing tips.

Echolocation calls (search flight) Two types of call can be distinguished: (a) short, sharply dropping FM signals from 80–38 kHz, duration 2–2.5 ms (see sonagram on page 211), with call sequence every 65–100 ms (approximately 10–15 signals per second); (b) flat, longer FM signal at 60–32 kHz, duration 4–5 ms (see sonagram on page 211), with call sequence every 100–110 ms (approximately 9–10 signals per second).

Further illustrations Pages 32, 201, 205.

Greater mouse-eared bat

Myotis myotis (Borkhausen, 1797)

G Grosses Mausohr   **F** Grand murin

Head–body (65) 67–79 (84) mm
Tail (40) 45–60 mm
Forearm 54–68 mm
Ear 26–31 mm
Wingspan 350–450 mm
Condylobasal length (21.5) 22–24 mm
Weight (20) 28–40 g

Identification Large. Nose short and broad, ears long and broad, outer edge with 7–8 transverse folds, front edge of ears distinctly bent backwards, ear tip broad. Tragus broad at base, reaches nearly halfway up ear. Fur dense and short, base of hairs brown, dorsal side light grey-brown, sometimes with rusty tinge. Ventral side white-grey. Nose, ears and wing membranes grey-brown. Juveniles darker, smokey-grey without brownish tinge. Wings broad, lateral membrane starts at base of toes. Calcar reaches half length of tail membrane, with narrow keel.

Colour anomalies Partial albinism (white wing tips).

Similar species Can be confused only with lesser mouse-eared bat; ears of latter are distinctly narrower and shorter (under 26 mm long), ear edge at front more in line; ear more pointed, tragus narrower. Nose narrower and more pointed, appears longer; the whole animal seems more delicate.

Distribution Central and southern Europe, absent in Ireland, Denmark and Scandinavia; in England now extinct; northern border of France, Belgium, Netherlands (faced with extinction), West Germany, East Germany, also reaches the Baltic Sea coast in Poland. In the south, Balkan and Mediterranean regions.

Status and protection Two small populations in England now extinct. Highly endangered in N.W. Europe, especially Netherlands, West Germany and Austria, but remnant populations have stabilized in many regions during the last few years. In nearly all parts of central Europe, populations have declined by 80% or more in the last 20–30 years. Specific protection of summer and winter roosts, and no use of wood preservatives that are toxic to warm-blooded animals; protection of habitat. Leave entrance holes in roosts (30 × 30 cm); if not possible even a slit sufficient.

Greater mouse-eared bat. When bats feel threatened they open their mouths wide, showing their sharp teeth; this is often accompanied by defensive noises.

Greater mouse-eared bat.

Habitat Prefers warmth. House-dwelling in the north, cave-dwelling in the south. Open countryside with trees, parks; dependent on areas of human settlement in the north. Mostly in caves below 600 m, in the summer up to 1920 m (Col de Bretolet, Alps), in winter up to 1460 m (Tatra Mountains, Poland). Summer roosts (nurseries) in the north in warm attics, in church towers (temperature up to 45 °C), very occasionally in warm rooms below ground. Individual animals also in nest boxes or tree holes. Winter roosts in caves, mine tunnels, cellars.

Temperature (3) 7–12 °C. Nearly always hangs free, but often in protected space in ceiling shafts, gaps in walls or cavities in cave roofs, rarely in narrow cracks. Often forms clusters. In the past up to many thousands in some hibernacula, but now rarely more than 100. Hibernation from September/October until beginning of March/April. Females appear in the hibernaculum before males. Change of roost site possible in winter; duration of each hibernation phase up to six weeks.

Migration Occasional migrant; distance between summer and winter roost in the north around 50 km, movement of more than 100 km not uncommon. Longest migration 390 km (Spain).

Reproduction A small percentage of females may reproduce as early as in their first year. Mating from August; one male can have a harem (up to five females); matings may take place in hibernacula. Nurseries as high up as 1000 m. The nurseries are occupied from March onwards, up to a maximum of 2000 females. During this time males live alone, occasionally individual males in nurseries. Births from beginning of June, usually in the early hours of morning; mothers leave the roost to hunt on their own on the same day. The babies are deposited together in groups, with some females staying behind with them in the roost. New-born bats pink; fine, hardly pigmented hairs on dorsal side. First day: weight c. 6 g, forearm 22.6 mm. Second week: weight 13 g, forearm 41.9 mm. 22nd day: weight 18–19 g, forearm 55.4 mm. Eyes open 4th–7th day, hair cover complete on 22nd day, adult teeth fully developed around 30th–35th day. Able to fly at 20–24 days, independent after 40 days (mid-July). High mortality rate has been recorded among young in cold weather (40% or above).

Maximum age 22 years. Average age 4–5 years.

Hunting and feeding Usually emerges only in darkness. Forages in parks, field and meadow areas, also near housing. Slow flight with 'rowing' wing beat, at 5–10 m height, but sometimes also close to the ground. Often lands on the ground to forage. Majority of prey consists of carabids, but also cockchafers, dung beetles, grasshoppers, crickets, moths, spiders.

Calls In the nurseries loud, shrill scolding and shrieking, when threatened also deep humming (like a large bumble-bee); sustained, loud screeching when disturbed during hibernation.

Echolocation calls (search flight) FM signals at 62–28 kHz (105–30 kHz). Duration 2–3 ms (about 12–20 signals per second) (see sonagram on page 211).

Further illustrations Pages 30, 49, 61, 66, 67, 201, 204.

Lesser mouse-eared bat
Myotis blythi (Tomes, 1857)

G Kleines Mausohr   **F** Petit murin

Head–body (54) 62–71 (76) mm
Tail 53–59 (60) mm
Forearm 52–59 (61.5) mm
Ear 19.8–23.5 (26) mm
Wingspan 350–400 mm
Condylobasal length 17.2–18.5 mm
Weight 15–28 g

Identification Very similar to greater mouse-eared bat, but a little smaller. Ears narrow and a bit shorter than those of latter, front edge of ear less strongly bent backwards, ear tapers off to more of a point; tragus base narrower, lancet-shaped, reaches nearly half length of ear; outer edge of ear with 5–6 transverse folds. Nose narrower and more pointed than that of greater mouse-eared bat, therefore seems longer. Fur short, base of hairs dark grey. Dorsal side grey with brownish tinge. Ventral side grey-white. Wing membrane starts at base of toes, calcar reaches about half of tail membrane length, small keel on calcar.

Colour anomalies Not known.

Distribution Southern Europe and Mediterranean region; northernmost part of range: Spain, S.E. France, isolated records in Switzerland and Austria, Czechoslovakia, Hungary, Romania, Moldavia and Ukraine.

Status and protection Faced with extinction in Austria, indications that numbers have also declined in S.E. Europe. Protection of caves and other roosts necessary.

Habitat Warm areas with not too dense tree and scrub cover, limestone areas, parks, also areas of human settlement; ecological differences from greater mouse-eared bat not precisely known; both species occur side by side. Recorded up to 1000 m. Summer roosts (nurseries) predominantly in warm caves, often shared with Schreiber's and horseshoe bats; but also occupy warm attics, hang free from roof rafters. Individual animals very occasionally in tree hollows. Winter roosts in caves and mine tunnels. Temperature 6–12 °C; mostly hang free.

Migration Occasional migratory species. Longest recorded movement 600 km (Spain).

Lesser mouse-eared
bat.

Lesser mouse-eared
bat.

Reproduction Mating in autumn, probably also until spring. One male can have a harem of females. Large nursery roosts of up to 5000 animals; mixed nurseries with greater mouse-eared bats have been encountered in attics. One young.

Maximum age 13 years.

Hunting and feeding Emerges at late dusk or even after dark. Flight slow, even, more agile in confined space than greater mouse-eared bat; probably takes prey off the ground occasionally. Preys on moths and beetles.

Calls Similar to greater mouse-eared bat; loud, shrill scolding or deep humming if threatened.

Further illustrations Pages 201, 204.

Genus: *Nyctalus* (Bodwich, 1825)

Six species, three of them found in Europe. Medium to large size, robust woodland bats with brown to reddish-brown fur. Ears short, triangular; tragus a broad mushroom-shape. Calcar with post-calcarial lobe which is divided by a clearly visible T-piece. Wings long and pointed. Two mammary glands.

Dental formula $\dfrac{2\ 1\ 2\ 3}{3\ 1\ 2\ 3} = 34$

Noctule
Nyctalus noctula (Schreber, 1774)

G Grosser Abendsegler   **F** Noctule commune

Head–body 60–82 (88) mm
Tail 41–60 mm
Forearm 47–58 mm
Ear 16–21 mm
Wingspan 320–400 mm
Condylobasal length 17.4–19.9 mm
Weight (17) 19–40 (46) g

Identification Large. Ears broad, triangular, tip rounded, outer edge with 4–5 transverse folds, much broader at base. Tragus short, mushroom-shaped. When mouth open, large glands are visible inside the corners of mouth especially in autumn. Fur short, flat-lying, hairs only one colour. Dorsal side rufous-brown and glossy in summer. Ventral side duller, lighter brown. After moult (August/September) dorsal side dull pale brown, sometimes with slight grey sheen. Juveniles dull brown on dorsal side, altogether darker. Ears, nose and wing membranes black-brown. Wings long and narrow, lateral membrane starts at heel, calcar reaches half length of tail membrane length; wide post-calcarial lobe with visible T-piece. Strong musky smell when irritated. May feign death, similar to pipistrelle bat, if disturbed when torpid during the day.

Colour anomalies Albinism.

Similar species Clear difference in size in comparison with Leisler's bat and greater noctule; Leisler's bat has dual-coloured hairs on dorsal side. Serotine: darker, tragus not mushroom-

The noctule (left) is one of Europe's largest bats. The whiskered bat (right), on the other hand, represents one of the smallest species.

shaped, post-calcarial lobe narrow, last one or two tail vertebrae free.

Distribution Throughout Europe except for Ireland, most of Scotland and N. Scandinavia. Reaches about 60° N. In the south, also in Balkan and Mediterranean areas, but virtually absent in Spain, Portugal and southern France.

Status and protection Now very rare in parts of Great Britain, particularly in agricultural areas. Threatened owing to felling of suitable trees with hollows (nursery and winter roosts) and destruction of winter roosts in buildings. If no suitable emergency roost is available immediately after a hibernaculum has been destroyed, the animals will have to be hibernated artificially, for example in a zoo. Lack of trees with suitable holes can be compensated for by putting up bat boxes.

Habitat Woodland bat; also in larger parks; predominantly in lowlands, during migration also up to 1920 m (Col de Bretolet, Alps). Summer roosts (nurseries) in tree holes (holes made by woodpeckers or caused by rot, splits in trunk), entrance hole round or slit-shaped, diameter 6 cm, diameter of hollow c. 12 cm, height of entrance hole above ground varies from 1–20 m. Sometimes occupies bat boxes. In summer, has also been observed in hollow concrete street lights, bridges and in gaps

135

between slabs of new blocks of houses. Hibernates in well-insulated tree hollows, deep rock crevices, buildings, cracks in house walls; in south-east Europe also in caves. Has been found in ventilation shafts of new buildings and in churches in larger cities. In large winter roosts up to 1000 animals. Temperature low, can also tolerate around 0 °C for short periods.

Hibernation from beginning of October/mid-November to mid-March/beginning of April. Loud, shrill calls can often be heard from inside a hibernaculum in rock or wall cracks, even if outside temperature is below 0 °C; in milder weather individual animals emerge. In the roost noctules form clusters, often sitting on top of each other like tiles on a roof. In harsh winters, up to 50% of the animals can freeze to death in unsuitable hibernacula.

Migration Migratory species; autumn migration in central Europe beginning in September/mid-November, main migration direction is S.W. Longest recorded movement, 930 km (in Soviet Union 1600 km). May also travel during the day and has been observed together with swallows. It is not known whether parts of the indigenous populations are sedentary.

Reproduction Females sexually mature in their first year, but sometimes give birth only in second year. Males participate in mating in their second year. Mating season from August to October. One male occupies a mating roost for several weeks (usually a tree-hole) and defends it against other, sexually mature males; emits mating calls near roost entrance or during flight, has a harem of 4–5 (20) females which stay with male for one or two days. Males not taking part in mating activities live together in groups. From April onwards, males and females in summer roosts; females in nursery roosts from mid-May, 20–50 females (up to several hundred); males outside the nurseries in small groups. Births mid-June/beginning of July, in England usually one but in central Europe usually two young, rarely three. Number of twin births is lowest in S.W. and increases towards N.E. Newly-born bats: naked, pink, weight 7.5 g, forearm 20 mm. 11th day: weight 10 g, forearm 32 mm. 36th day: weight 15 g, forearm 45 mm. Eyes open 3rd–6th day; at 14 days completely covered with grey to silvery-grey hair; this changes colour to brown at 36 days. Able to fly from 4th week; adult teeth complete from 5th–7th week, then independent.

Maximum age 12 years.

Hunting and feeding Emerges early, sometimes even before sunset. Duration of hunting flight 1–1.5 hours, in summer may hunt again before sunrise. Flight fast (up to 50 km/h), high above ground (10–40 m and up to 70 m), in a straight line with fast

136

Noctule bat. As with all vesper bats, the eyeslit is hardly visible when the bat's eyes are closed.

turns and dives, wings nearly touch beneath body during flight. Its flight silhouette has long, slender, often distinctly angular wings and wedge-shaped tail membrane, the latter with smooth back edge if spread out. Forages above meadows, lakes, refuse tips, also above tree tops; hunting ground up to 6 km from roost. Preys on moths, cockchafers and other larger flying insects.

Calls Near nursery roosts or winter roosts high-pitched, loud scolding or twittering can be heard at intervals.

Echolocation calls (search flight) Two types of call can be distinguished (see sonagram on page 212). (a) FM signal at 45–25 kHz; duration 6 ms; highest pulse intensity at 25 kHz; call sequence every 125 ms (8 signals per second); used when hunting at low height. (b) Long flat signal at 25–19 kHz; duration 25 ms; call sequence every 300–400 ms (3 signals per second). When hunting above tree-tops both types of call are used regularly and interchangeably. Very loud calls. Range up to 200 m.

Social calls During flight loud, short metallic-sounding signals ('zick' or 'bick') that can be heard up to 50 m away and are nearly painful if heard in the immediate vicinity; 32–17 kHz; rising and falling 14 times in 110 ms.

Further illustration Page 27.

Leisler's bat
Nyctalus leisleri (Kuhl, 1818)

G Kleiner Abendsegler **F** Noctule de Leisler

Head–body 48–68 mm
Tail 35–45 mm
Forearm (37) 38–47 mm
Ear 12–16 mm
Wingspan 260–320 mm
Condylobasal length 14.7–16 mm
Weight 11–20 g

Identification Medium-sized. Ear conch and tragus like noctule, outer ear edge with 4–5 transverse folds; nose slightly more pointed. Fur short, hairs dual-coloured, black-brown at base. Dorsal side rufous-brown, usually slightly darker and less shiny than noctule's. Ventral side yellow-brown. Face, ears and wing membranes black-brown. Juveniles altogether darker. Wings long and narrow, wing membranes covered with dense hair along body and arms, lateral membrane starts at heel. Calcar and post-calcarial lobe like noctule.

Colour anomalies Not known.

Similar species Noctule: larger, hair only one colour. Nathusius' pipistrelle: smaller, tragus not mushroom-shaped.

Distribution Nearly all over Europe, but only sporadic records in whole area except Ireland where it is common and widespread. Occurs in England and Wales, eastern France, Netherlands, West Germany, East Germany, Poland and Soviet Union. Does not appear to reach the coasts of North and Baltic Seas, absent in Scandinavia. Absent in Portugal, rare in Spain and Italy, and occurs in Balkan countries.

Status and protection Rare everywhere except Ireland. Protection measures similar to noctule, erecting of bat boxes.

Habitat Woodland bat; similar to noctule, in summer up to 1920 m (Col de Bretolet, Alps). Summer roosts (nurseries) in buildings and tree holes, as well as bat boxes, sometimes together with noctule bats. Hibernacula in tree holes, cracks and cavities on and in buildings; hibernates in larger groups. Hibernation from end of September until beginning of April.

Migration Migratory species. Longest recorded movement 810 km. Movements probably from N.E. to S.E.

Leisler's bat.

Reproduction No information on beginning of sexual maturity. Mating season end of August/September. Male has mating roost and harem of up to nine females. Nursery size in tree holes 20–50 females, in buildings up to 500 animals (Ireland). Births from mid-June. Single young usual in west, twins recorded in east.

Maximum age 9 years.

Leisler's bat.

Hunting and feeding Similar to noctule. Emerges shortly after sunset. Flight fast, high, often with dives. Preys on moths, beetles and other flying insects.

Calls Short, shrill, similar to those of noctule.

Further illustration Page 199.

Greater noctule
Nyctalus lasiopterus (Schreber, 1780)

G Riesenabendsegler **F** Noctule géante

Head–body 84–104 mm
Tail 55–65 mm
Forearm 63–69 mm
Ear 21–26 mm
Wingspan 410–460 mm
Condylobasal length 22–23.6 mm
Weight 41–76 g

Identification Largest European bat. Ear similar to noctule, but broader; sparse hairs on widened ear-edge at back; tragus mushroom-shaped. Fur dense and relatively long, hairs of only one colour. Dorsal side reddish-brown, usually darker than noctule; ventral side yellow-brown. Juveniles of darker colour. Nose and ears black-brown. Wings long and narrow, rusty-coloured hairs on wing undersides along body. Start of lateral membrane, calcar and post-calcarial lobe as for noctule.

Colour anomalies Not known.

Similar species Noctule, but this is distinctly smaller.

Distribution Only partially known, apparently mainly S.E. Europe; records from Spain, Portugal, France, Italy, Switzerland, Austria, Czechoslovakia, Poland, Hungary, Romania, Bulgaria, European part of Soviet Union, Yugoslavia, Albania and Greece. In most cases only single records.

Status and protection Status in Europe uncertain. It is commoner in Asia. As far as can be assessed owing to the small amount of information available, the situation is similar to that of the other two noctule species.

Habitat Woodland bat; often in deciduous woods, recorded up to 1920 m (Col de Bretolet, Alps). Summer roosts in Soviet Union often shared with noctule, Nathusius' pipistrelle or pipistrelle bats. Nursery roosts and hibernacula in tree holes.

Migration Migratory species; animals living in Byelorussia migrate S.E. in autumn.

Reproduction No precise information about start of sexual maturity and mating season; probably similar to noctule. Only small nursery roosts (up to 10 females), sometimes shared with

Greater noctule bat.

species mentioned above. Births from end of June. One or two young. Newly-born: weight 5–7 g, forearm 20–26 mm. 10th day: forearm 30–35 mm. 20th day: forearm 40–45 mm. Forearm no longer grows after 40th day. By then fur like adults, also able to fly at around that age.

Maximum age Not known.

Hunting and feeding No precise information, probably similar to noctule.

Further illustration Page 199.

Genus: *Eptesicus* Rafinesque, 1820

Thirty species, two of them in Europe. Ears and nose black, one or two tail vertebrae extend beyond tail membrane. Calcar with narrow post-calcarial lobe. Wings relatively broad. Two mammary glands.

Dental formula $\dfrac{2\ 1\ 1\ 3}{3\ 1\ 2\ 3} = 32$

Serotine
Eptesicus serotinus (Schreber, 1774)

G Breitflügelfledermaus   **F** Sérotine commune

Head–body 62–82 mm
Tail (39) 46–54 (59) mm
Forearm 48–57 mm
Ear (12) 14–22 mm
Wingspan 315–380 mm
Condylobasal length 18–21.2 mm
Weight 14–33 (35) g

Identification Large; ears relatively short, nearly triangular, outer ear-edge narrow, five transverse folds; points in direction of corner of mouth, but ending shortly before. Tragus up to approximately one-third of ear length, bent slightly inwards, rounded at top. Fur long, base of hair dark-brown. Dorsal side dark smokey-brown, slight variations, hair tips sometimes slightly shiny. Ventral side yellow-brown; border dorsal/ventral side blurred. Juveniles darker altogether. Ears and nose black, wing membranes dark black-brown. Wings broad, lateral membrane starts at base of toes, last one or two tail vertebrae free (5–8 mm); calcar reaches about one-third to one-half of tail membrane length; narrow post-calcarial lobe without visible T-piece. Quiet temperament.

Colour anomalies Occasional records of albinism.

Similar species Not easily confused with other species. Northern and parti-coloured bats: smaller, different colour on dorsal side. Noctule: rufous-brown, tragus mushroom-shaped. Greater and lesser mouse-eared bats: dorsal side greyer, ear and tragus longer and of different shape.

Distribution All over Europe, up to 55° N. (southern Wales and southern England, Denmark, southern Sweden), in the south, Mediterranean and Balkan regions, as far as Caucasus Mountains.

Status and protection Declining in abundance but apparently increasing its range northwards. Threatened in particular by chemical woodworm treatments, disturbance and the loss of nursery roost sites; wood preservatives toxic to warm-blooded creatures should not be used.

Habitat House-dwelling bat, mainly in lowlands, in areas of human settlements with parks, gardens, meadows, at the edges of big towns. Recorded up to 900 m above sea level (summer), and 1100 m (winter). Summer roosts (nurseries) often in ridge timbers or hollow walls, usually not hanging free but rather hidden behind boarding or beams. Individual animals (usually males) also in gaps between roof beams, behind facia boards and weather boarding, rarely in nest or bat boxes, in southern Europe also in limestone caves. Winter roosts in caves, mine tunnels, cellars, also in deep gaps between roof timbers, behind pictures in churches, in piles of wood. Although a fairly common species no large scale roosts are known; usually solitary males are found, either wedged in cracks or hanging free on roofs and walls and also in gravel on the ground. Temperature 2–4 °C; humidity relatively low. Hibernation from about October to end of March/April.

Serotine bat.

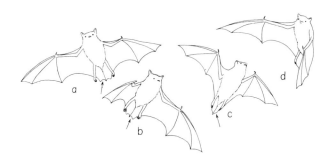

With some practice, species of similar size, serotine (**a, b**) and noctule (**c, d**) can be distinguished in flight. The faster noctule shows narrower, often clearly angled wings and a wedge-shaped tail; the serotine has broad wings and a short tail, either rounded or with many points (based on Lawitter and Vierhaus, 1975).

Migration Difficult to categorize, probably fairly sedentary species. Records of journeys over 83, 145, 204 and 330 km indicate, however, that the serotine may be an occasional migrant.

Reproduction Females sexually mature in their first year (in Soviet Union). Mating season from end of August; not known if it lasts until spring. Nursery roosts are occupied from April/May, 10–50 (100) females; if disturbed the animals run very fast into the hollow gaps of roof ridge. Males are solitary throughout year. Births from second half of June, in Europe one young (in Central Asia two, rarely three). Newly-born: weight 5.2–6.2 g, forearm c. 21 mm. Weight doubled by approximately 10th day. Growth of forearm completed after about five weeks. Eyes open after 7–8 days, adult teeth complete at end of third week, young bats can then also fly. The young are independent at about five weeks (end July/beginning August). Dispersal of nursery roosts end of August.

Maximum age 19 years 3 months.

Hunting and feeding Emergence in early dusk. Flight slow (15, max. 30 km/h), at 6–10 m above ground flies in large loops in gardens along woodland edges, above rubbish tips, around street lights. Usually silent during flight, the broad wings are hardly angled, the tail membrane appears rounded not wedge-shaped, and seems to be short with many little points. Sometimes two foraging trips in one night, distance between roost and hunting ground rarely more than 1 km. Catches moths as well as beetles. Since serotine bats in captivity react with searching behaviour

145

to imitations of the rustling noises produced by moving beetles, it seems possible that they may also pick prey off branches or off the ground. Emerges to hunt even in slight drizzle.

Calls In defence loud, high chirping or 'tsicking' calls.

Echolocation calls (searching flight) FM signals at (67) 52–25 kHz; duration 13.5 ms (see sonagram on page 212). Highest pulse intensity at 25 kHz; call sequence every 150 ms (6.7 signals per second); range 20–50 m.

Further illustrations Pages 23, 203, 207.

Serotine bat.

Northern bat

Eptesicus nilssonii (Keyserling et Blasius, 1839)

G Nordfledermaus   **F** Sérotine de Nilsson

Head–body (45) 54–64 mm
Tail 35–50 mm
Forearm (37) 38–44 mm
Ear (11.5) 13.0–17.5 mm
Wingspan 240–280 mm
Condylobasal length 14–15.2 (15.6) mm
Weight (6.5) 8–18 g

Identification Medium-sized. Ears relatively short, outer ear-edge with five transverse folds, gets broader towards base and nearly reaches corner of mouth; tragus short, broad, slightly bent towards inside, rounded on top. Fur long, base of hairs dark-brown. Hair tips on dorsal side with golden sheen, hairs with golden sheen also on crown; neck darker, only here relatively sharp border with yellow-brown ventral side. Juveniles darker, dorsal side without golden sheen, hair tips appear more silvery, belly grey. Nose, ears and wing membranes black-brown, calcar reaches about half length of tail membrane; narrow post-calcarial lobe. Last tail vertebra free (3–4 mm). Lateral membrane starts at base of toes.

Colour anomalies Not known.

Similar species Savi's pipistrelle bat: very little size overlap, tragus broadens towards top, outer edge of ear hardly broader, belly and throat more white. Parti-coloured bat: outer edge of ear clearly broader, in different alignment, throat white, hair tips on dorsal side silvery, distinct post-calcarial lobe.

Distribution Northern, central and eastern Europe; only European bat species to reach the Arctic Circle, all of Scandinavia, Estonia and Lithuania; East Germany and southern West Germany, Switzerland, Austria, Czechoslovakia, Hungary, Poland.

Status and protection Occurs in Great Britain as a vagrant only. Specific protection of known nursery roosts similar to serotine .

Habitat In central Europe, predominantly in foothills of mountains or in medium-high mountainous regions, areas of fairly open scrub and woodland, also in areas of human settlement, in the mountains up to 2290 m or more above sea

147

level (Alps), in winter 2200 m (in caves). Summer roosts usually in cracks, nursery roosts frequently on or in houses covered with slate or sheet metal, behind chimney cladding, shutters, in cracks in roof timbering. Single animals also in tree holes and wood piles. Winter roosts in caves, mine tunnels, cellars; temperature 1–5.5 °C (7.5), temporarily (1–2 days) down to −5.5 °C. Found hanging free from walls or roofs or wedged in crevices; does not form clusters. Hibernation from October until March/April; regional differences.

Migration No precise information, probably sedentary. Furthest recorded movement 115 km.

Reproduction Very little known; about 20–60 females in nursery roosts. Nurseries occupied from end April, frequent changes of roost site. Births from second half of June (Czechoslovakia). In north and the Soviet Union usually two young, in Czechoslovakia normally one. Young able to fly mid- to end of July.

Maximum age 14.5 years.

Hunting and feeding Emergence in early dusk, sometimes only after dark. Flight rapid, agile with fast turns. Usually hunts in open areas with wide open air space, above water; also at tree-top height; hangs on branches to rest; hunts even in fine drizzle. Preys on flying insects.

Northern bat.

Echolocation calls (searching flight) FM signals from 38–28 kHz, end in CF signals at 30 kHz. Duration 10–12 ms (see sonagram on page 212). Highest pulse intensity at 30 kHz. Call sequence every 200 ms (5 signals per second). Range up to 50 m. Similar calls to parti-coloured bat and noctule bat (low-hunting).

Social calls Sharp loud pulses at 58–10 kHz ending in CF components (up to 10 ms).

Further illustration Page 201.

Genus: *Vespertilio* Linnaeus, 1758

Three species, one of them in Europe.

Dental formula $\dfrac{2\ 1\ 1\ 3}{3\ 1\ 2\ 3} = 32$

Parti-coloured bat
Vespertilio murinus Linnaeus, 1758

G Zweifarbfledermaus **F** Sérotine bicolor

Head–body 48–64 mm
Tail 37–44.5 mm
Forearm 39–49 mm
Ear 12–16.5 (18.8) mm
Wingspan 270–310 mm
Condylobasal length 13.9–15.7 (16.2) mm
Weight 12–20.5 g

Identification Medium-sized. Ears short, broad, slightly rounded, outer ear-edge with four transverse folds, extends with wide fold to below the line of the corner of the mouth and then comes back up to it again; tragus short, broadens towards top, reaches its greatest width around the second third of its length, rounded at top. Fur long, dense. Base of hairs black-brown, with silvery-white tips on dorsal side, hence 'frosted' appearance. Ventral side white-grey, throat nearly pure white, sharp contrast to dorsal side. Ears, wing membranes and nose black-brown. Juveniles darker, more grey-black, hair tips dirty grey-white, belly yellowish-white. Wings narrow, lateral membrane starts at base of toes, calcar longer than half length of tail membrane, distinct post-calcarial lobe. Last two tail vertebrae free (3.5–5 mm). Only European bat to possess two pairs of mammary glands, 4–5 mm apart from each other.

Colour anomalies Not known.

Similar species Northern and serotine bats. Barbastelle bat: similar colouring of dorsal side, but completely different ear shape, ventral side dark.

Distribution Central and eastern Europe, up to around 60° N., often only single records; southern Sweden, southern Norway, more frequent in Denmark, Estonia, West Germany; mainly individual records in East Germany; Switzerland, eastern France, northern Italy, one nursery roost known in Czechoslovakia, Balkans. Two recent records from England. July 1978 discovery of a large nursery roost by Hinkel and Zoellick on the Baltic Sea coast N.W. of Rostock (East Germany). Reproduction: nurseries mostly in northern and eastern Europe, with hibernation in south and west.

Status and protection Occurs in Great Britain as a vagrant only. Under extreme threat or rare over much of range. Endangered migratory species. Protective measures pose problems since little information on species is available, protection of sites of known roosts.

Habitat Originally probably a bat of cliff habitats. In wooded hilly areas and steppe regions, also in large cities on tower blocks (cliff substitute?). In mountains up to 1920 m (Col de Bretolet, Alps). Summer roosts mainly in cracks, for example behind window shutters, in walls, in cavities of wooden houses and in attics. Winter roosts in caves, cellars, mostly hidden away in crevices, possibly also in tree hollows. Hibernation October to March.

Parti-coloured bat.

Parti-coloured bat.

Migration Migratory species, movements from N.E. towards S.W. (hibernacula); animals leave Byelorussia in August. Movements up to 900 km.

Reproduction Only fragmentary information. Mating season from August, male testes greatly enlarged during this time. Nursery roosts of 30–50 females. Births end of June/beginning of July. Two young, less often three. Males form large colonies in summer (up to 250 animals or more).

Maximum age 5 years.

Hunting and feeding Emerge in late dusk. Flight high (10–20 m above ground), fast, in a straight line. Hunts throughout the night. Catches beetles and moths.

Echolocation calls (searching flight) Several types of call (see sonagram on page 212): (a) FM signal at 50–20 kHz; duration 5–8 ms; highest impulse intensity at 25 kHz; call sequence every 180–200 ms (5–6 signals per second). (b) A loud CF 'shout', dropping by 2 kHz. (c) Undulating signals of 40 ms duration.

Social calls Loud, shrill mating calls in autumn are known. They last about 150 ms, start off with 12 FM signals that repeat themselves in quick succession (30–16 kHz), followed by a shout (50–14 kHz) turning into a CF signal at 14 kHz (c. 10 ms), then a drop in frequency to 10 kHz. Call sequence every 235 ms (4.3 mating calls per second).

Further illustration Page 203.

Genus: *Pipistrellus* Kaup, 1829

About 48 species, four of them in Europe; small, short ears, tragus rounded, calcar with post-calcarial lobe; nose, ears and wing membranes dark, wings relatively narrow; two mammary glands.

Dental formula $\dfrac{2\ 1\ 2\ 3}{3\ 1\ 2\ 3} = 34$

Pipistrelle
Pipistrellus pipistrellus (Schreber, 1774)

G Zwergfledermaus   **F** Pipistrelle commune

Head–body (32) 36–51 mm
Tail (20) 23–36 mm
Forearm 28–35 mm
Ear 9–13.5 mm
Wingspan 180–240 mm
Condylobasal length 11–11.8 mm
5th finger 36–42 mm
Weight 3.5–8.5 g

Identification Smallest European bat. Ears short, triangular, rounded tip, outer ear-edge with 4–5 transverse folds, tragus longer than it is wide, slightly bent inwards, rounded at top. Base of hair dark to black-brown. Dorsal side rufous-brown, chestnut-brown or dark-brown. Ventral side yellow-brown to grey-brown. Nose, ears and wing membranes black-brown. Juveniles darker and greyer. Free edge of wing membrane between 5th finger and foot occasionally with narrow, pale imprecisely delimited border. Wings narrow, lateral membrane starts at base of toes; calcar reaches approximately one-third of tail membrane length, distinct post-calcarial lobe with transverse T-shaped cartilage. Lower leg and tail membrane without hair. Dentition: P^1 small, pushed inwards from the line of the tooth row, I^2 usually shorter than small tip of I^1. Glandular swellings inside corners of mouth especially in autumn. If disturbed during hibernation or when torpid during the day, animals may feign death.

Colour anomalies Partial albinism (skin and flight membranes white, fur white or a light yellow-brownish colour, dark eyes).

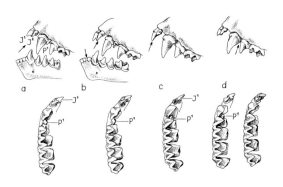

Tooth rows of *Pipistrellus* species (viewed from outside and above). **a.** Pipistrelle; **b.** Nathusius' pipistrelle; **c.** Kuhl's pipistrelle; **c.** Savi's pipistrelle. **I** Incisors; **P¹** Ist premolar in upper jaw (for further details see species description and identification key).

Pipistrelle bat. The comparison with the size of the human thumb illustrates clearly that it is one of the smallest mammals in Europe.

Similar species Nathusius' pipistrelle bat: 5th finger relatively longer, tail membrane covered with hairs up to centre on dorsal side and along the lower legs on ventral side. Kuhl's and Savi's pipistrelles: usually larger, note differences in colouring and tooth characteristics; Savi's pipistrelle has different tragus shape. Whiskered bat: ear and tragus completely different.

Distribution Nearly all over Europe, up to about $61' \div$ N.; Ireland, Great Britain, southern Scandinavia, in the south as far as Mediterranean and Balkan regions, in the east as far as Caucasus Mountains.

Status and protection Still one of the most common bat species in northern and central Europe. By far the commonest bat in Great Britain. Widespread and common throughout the country but has declined by 60% in the past 10 years. Protection of nursery roosts. Cats catch many bats at roost. Erection of bat boarding or bat boxes, leave window shutters in place.

Habitat Predominantly house-dwelling species; in villages and cities; in parks and woodlands. Nursery roosts usually below 600 m, animals recorded up to maximum of 2000 m above sea level. Summer roosts (nurseries) in cracks accessible from outside, behind board cladding, panelling, shutters, in timber-framed buildings, also in bat boxes. Individuals in wall crevices and behind noticeboards. Winter roosts in all kinds of places including trees and buildings, in northern and central Europe in large churches (up to 2000 animals), in old chalk pits, deep rock crevices, wall cracks, in cellars. In a cave in Romania about 100,000 animals were found hanging free on the roof in large clusters. Relatively insensitive to cold, temperature 0–6 °C, occasionally changes hibernaculum; duration of sleeping phases during hibernation 1–4 weeks. Hibernation from mid-November to beginning of March/April.

Migration Most populations in central Europe are sedentary; distance between summer and winter roosts usually about 10–20 (50) km. Longest recorded movements were of two females ringed in northern East Germany, one was recovered 770 km S.W. and the other 540 km S.E. A bat in Great Britain moved 69 km N.E. from Suffolk to Norfolk. (The journey of 1160 km from the Ukraine to southern Bulgaria frequently quoted in the literature is a result of a confusion with Nathusius' pipistrelle bat.) The reason for some animals undertaking long journeys is not known.

Reproduction Females and some males become mature in their first year, males generally in their second. Even during the nursery season males occupy individually established territories and defend these during the mating season (end of August to end of September) against other males. They emit special social calls during mating flights and smell strongly of musk. Females visit mating roosts temporarily. One male has a harem of up to 10 females. Nursery roosts are occupied in April/May, and can be shared with Nathusius' pipistrelles, 20–250 (to over 1000) females. Births mid-June/beginning of July. In central Europe usually two young, proportion of twin births increases from W. and S. towards E. and N.; in Great Britain normally only one young. Newly-born: dorsal side pinkish, weight 1–1.4 g, forearm 11–12 mm. 10th day: forearm 16–17 mm. 20th day: forearm 23–25.5 mm. 30th day: weight 4–4.3 g, forearm 27–28.6 mm, wingspan 170–180 mm. Eyes open at 3–5 days, adult teeth at four weeks, able to fly at 3–4 weeks. Nursery roosts usually abandoned by adult females in August, and by juveniles in August or September; during this period in central and northern Europe so-called invasions often occur in high, large rooms, also flats, involving up to 100 mainly juvenile pipistrelle bats (young generation of a nursery searching for roost?). Some nursery clusters move frequently between roosts.

Maximum age 16 years 7 months. Average age 4 years.

Hunting and feeding Emergence early, sometimes before sunset, in late autumn also during the day. Flight rapid, agile, 5–10 m above ground. Hunts 1–2 km from roost above ponds, along woodland edges, in gardens, around street lights; often follows fixed flight paths. Catches small moths, gnats and other insects. Often returns to roost after only 1–2 hours but may feed intermittently throughout night.

Calls Shrill scolding when disturbed.

Echolocation calls (searching flight) Two types of call (see sonagram on page 213).

(a) Most frequent type short FM signal at 80–58 kHz; 4–6 ms, may end in pure CF component; highest pulse intensity at 58 kHz; call sequence every 85 ms (12 signals per second). When flying in groups, the CF component may vary between animals by 14 kHz. (b) Pure CF signal at 51 kHz of 10 ms duration; call sequence every 95 ms (10.5 signals per second). Both call types are not used alternately as is the case with the noctule bat. Range 20–50 m.

Social calls Undulating loud shout between 35–18 kHz, rising and falling four times in 35 ms.

Further illustrations Pages 46, 55, 56, 69, 79, 203, 205, 209.

Pipistrelle bat. A one-day old baby is hidden below the bulging flight membrane; only foot and forearm are visible. Note that the baby's foot is nearly as large as the mother's.

Nathusius' pipistrelle
Pipistrellus nathusii (Keyserling and Blasius, 1839)

G Rauhhautfledermaus   **F** Pipistrelle de Nathusius

Head–body 46–55 (58) mm
Tail (30) 32–40 (44) mm
Forearm 32–37 mm
Ear 10–14 mm
Wingspan 220–250 mm
Condylobasal length (12.1) 12.3–13.2 mm
5th finger (42) 43–48 mm
Weight 6–15.5 g

Identification Small. Ear short, triangular, tip rounded, outer edge of ear with 4–5 transverse folds, tragus short, slightly bent inwards, tip rounded. Base of hair dark brown. Dorsal side red to chestnut brown in summer, after moult (July/August) darker brown, often with obvious grey tips. Ventral side light brown to yellow-brown. Tail, ears and flight membranes black-brown. Juveniles dark brown without grey tones. Wings long, free edge of wing membrane between 5th finger and foot often with narrow, not sharply delimited, light edge, lateral membrane starts at base of toes. Tail membrane hairy on upper side up to half length and on underside along lower leg. Calcar reaches approximately one-third length of tail membrane, post-calcarial lobe with obvious T-shaped cartilage. Dentition: P^1 well developed, visible from outside, I^2 longer than short tip of I^1. Feigns death like pipistrelle.

Colour anomalies Record of one animal with ash-grey fur.

Similar species As for pipistrelle.

Distribution Eastern regions of southern and central Europe; in England only three records, but several from oil rigs in North Sea. In the north of Europe: widespread in Netherlands; Denmark, southern Sweden, along Baltic coast as far as Leningrad area. In the south of Europe: Mediterranean coast and Balkan region; also on Corsica; Caucasus. Not found in Iberian peninsula.

Status and protection Greatly endangered in West Germany, endangered in Austria and East Germany; populations which have been monitored over many years in the north of East Germany, however, remain stable. Certainly commoner in many areas than so far realized, since this species has been recorded particularly during specific research on woodland bats (bat boxes). The erection of narrow boxes or bat boarding on hunting towers has been very successful.

Habitat Woodland bat; both in damp deciduous woods and dry pine forests, parks; less often in areas of human settlement, prefers lowlands; on migration up to 1920 m (Col de Bretolet, Alps). Summer roosts (nursery roosts) in hollow trees, bat boxes, cracks in trees, crevices on hunting towers, more rarely in buildings; overall prefers cracks; sometimes shares nursery roost with pipistrelle or Brandt's bat. Hibernates in crevices in cliffs, cracks in walls, caves and hollow trees.

Migration Migratory species; from around mid-August/September the whole of the population resident in the north of East Germany migrates towards the S.W. (France, Switzerland, West Germany), returning to their summer roosts in April/May. Several recorded instances of bats migrating over 1000 km (max. 1600 km). The females migrate earlier in autumn than the males. Hibernation sites are known in West Germany, Austria and Switzerland, but none has so far been discovered in Poland, East Germany or Czechoslovakia.

Reproduction Females become sexually mature in first year, males not until second year. Mating season from second half

Nathusius' pipistrelle in rufous-brown summer pelage.

July to beginning of September; testes and epididymis of males visibly increase in size; notable glandular swellings on nose. The males have mating territories, harems of 3–10 females. Behaviour in mating territory similar to that of pipistrelle. The nursery roosts are occupied in April/May, 50–200 females. Young females often return the following year to the nursery roosts of their birth. Strong loyalty to their territory, although several changes of nursery roost site possible during the summer. Births in second half July, rarely earlier. Two young. Newly-born: pink, weight 1.6–1.8 g, forearm 12–13.5 mm. 10th day: weight 3.2–4.5 g, forearm 17.5–20 mm. 20th day: weight 5.2 g, forearm 28 mm. Eyes open on 3rd day; can fly at around four weeks; mothers leave the nursery roost from mid-July onwards and seek out the mating roosts which may be up to 15 km away.

Maximum age 7 years.

Hunting and feeding Emerges in early dusk. Flight rapid, often deep wing beats when flying in straight line; in confined spaces

The winter fur of Nathusius' pipistrelle bat, which grows after moulting, is darker brown, with light grey tips

not so manoeuverable as pipistrelle. Forages 4–15 m above ground along rides, paths and woodland edges, and also over water. Preys on small to medium-large flying insects.

Calls When disturbed, high-pitched scolding like pipistrelle; sharp whispering can often be heard from occupied bat boxes.

Echolocation calls (search flight) FM signals ending in CF component, 70–38 kHz; duration 5 ms (see sonagram page 213); call sequence every 100–125 ms (c. 8–10 signals per second).

Further illustrations Pages 24, 53, 154, 203, 205, 209.

Kuhl's pipistrelle

Pipistrellus kuhli (Kuhl, 1819)

G Weissrandfledermaus   **F** Pipistrelle de Kuhl

head–body 40–47 (48) mm
Tail 30–34 mm
Forearm 31–36 (37) mm
Ear 12–13 mm
Wingspan 210–240 mm
Condylobasal length 12–13.2 mm
Weight 5–10 g

Identification Small, ears short, roughly triangular, rounded at tip, outer edge with five transverse folds. Tragus not wider at tip, rounded, slightly bent inwards. Fur colouring very variable, base of hair dark brown. Dorsal side medium brown to yellow-brown, also light cinnamon brown. Ventral side light grey to grey-white. Ears, flight membranes and nose dark to black-brown. Wings relatively narrow; start of lateral membranes at base of toes; free edge of lateral membrane particularly between 5th finger and foot with 1–2 mm wide white edge, which is only rarely absent. Calcar with post-calcarial lobe divided by a T-shaped cartilage. Dentition: I^1 with one point, I^2 very small, P^1 set inside tooth row and not visible from outside. Conspicuous glands inside corners of mouth.

Colour anomalies A rare colour variation is dark grey-brown to black-brown on the dorsal side. Ventral side only a little lighter. Can always be identified by examining teeth.

Similar species Savi's pipistrelle bat: tip of tail free of membrane by 3–5 mm, tragus shorter, wider in upper part; dentition: I^1 two points, see section on this species for more details.

Distribution S. and S.W. Europe, Portugal, Spain, most of France, Switzerland, Austria, Italy, Yugoslavia, Greece, Mediterranean islands, to E. in Caucasus.

Status and protection Almost impossible to quantify extent of threat in its main distribution range. Spreading northwards. Specific protection of known summer roosts.

Habitat Both in lowlands and lower mountain areas; relatively closely associated with areas of human settlement, but also in areas of limestone. Summer roosts (nursery roosts) predominantly in crevices on and in buildings (cracks in walls, gaps under

Kuhl's pipistrelle.

the roof), single animals also in cracks in cliffs. Hibernacula, as far as is known, crevices in cliffs and cellars.

Migration Not known, probably sedentary.

Reproduction Females sexually mature in first year. Small nursery colonies with around 20 females. Two young.

Maximum age 8 years.

Hunting and feeding Emerges in late dusk or in darkness. Forages at low or medium height above ground around street lamps, over water surfaces, in gardens. Flight rapid and agile. Preys on small flying insects.

Further illustrations Pages 154, 203.

162

Savi's pipistrelle

Pipistrellus savii (Bonaparte, 1837)

G Alpenfledermaus   **F** Pipistrelle de Savi

Head–body 40–54 mm
Tail 31–43 mm
Forearm 30–37 (38) mm
Ear (10) 12–15 mm
Wingspan 220–250 mm
Condylobasal length 11.9–13.6 (14) mm
Weight 5–10 g

Identification Is classified by Horacek and Hanak as a separate genus *Hypsugo*; morphologically it is between the genera *Eptesicus* and *Pipistrellus*. Small. Ears wider and rounder than those of other European *Pipistrellus* species, outer edge of ear with four transverse folds; tragus short, widens somewhat in upper part, the length of its edge part is almost equivalent to its largest width; at base of outer edge two serrations one above the other, the rounded tip of the tragus is directed inwards. Fur relatively long, base of hair black-brown. Dorsal side varies from pale yellow-brown or gold-brown to dark brown with glossy gold tips. Ventral side pale white-yellowish to grey-white, clear contrast between ventral and dorsal side. Ears and nose black-brown or black, clear contrast to other colouring; flight membranes dark brown. Lateral membrane starts at base of toes, calcar with narrow post-calcarial lobe; last one or two vertebrae free (3–5 mm). Dentition: I^1 with two cusps, P^1 not visible from outside, displaced inwards in the tooth row, completely missing in 10–40% of animals. Very lively behaviour.

Colour anomalies Not known.

Similar species Savi's pipistrelle, pipistrelle and Nathusius' pipistrelle bats: see relevant sections. Northern bat: similar colouring, but larger.

Distribution Predominantly southern Europe: Spain, southern France, Switzerland, Italy, Yugoslavia, Bulgaria, Greece.

Status and protection Greatly endangered in West Germany, no recent records and very possibly extinct in Austria. Accurate assessment not possible because of lack of data.

Habitat Mountain valleys, alpine pastures, limestone areas, on Mediterranean islands found along coasts; also in areas of human settlement; in mountains records up to 2600 m above sea

163

level. Summer roosts (nursery roosts) often in crevices in and on buildings (roof timbers, cracks in walls, cavities between bricks, holes in walls), crevices in cliffs. Winter roosts in lower-lying valleys in cliff cracks, in caves, probably also in tree holes.

Migration Not possible to say with certainty because of lack of specific research. Probably occasional migrant, furthest record over 250 km.

Reproduction Knowledge only fragmentary. Mating season from around end August/September. Nursery roosts with 20–70 females. Births mid-June to beginning July, two young.

Maximum age Not known.

Hunting and feeding Emergence shortly after sunset. Flight

Savi's pipistrelle.

Savi's pipstrelle.

straight, even, not very quick, sometimes above houses and tree tops. Forages nearly all night. On islands in the Adriatic, emergence has been observed from cliffs even during the day, followed by flight close over the surface of the sea. Preys on small flying insects.

Further illustrations Pages 154, 203.

Genus: *Plecotus* Geoffroy, 1818

Five species, two of them in Europe. Ears longer than 30 mm, joined together by a skin fold at the base on the front; nostrils open upwards. Echolocation calls are emitted through nose with mouth closed. Calcar without post-calcarial lobe.

Dental formula $\dfrac{2\ 1\ 2\ 3}{3\ 1\ 3\ 3} = 36$

Long-eared bat
Plecotus auritus (Linnaeus, 1758)

G Braunes Langohr **F** Oreillard commun

Head–body 42–53 (55) mm
Tail (32) 37–55 mm
Forearm 34–42 mm
Ear 31–41 (43) mm
Wingspan 240–285 mm
Condylobasal length (13.2) 14–15.6 mm
Weight 5–12 g

Identification Medium-sized. Strikingly long ears, ear conch thin, 22–24 transverse folds, inner ear-edge broadened, with a fringe of fine hairs, knob-like projection near ear base. Ears erected only shortly before flying off and in flight, otherwise folded and held backwards (reminiscent of ram horns); when torpid or hibernating folded and tucked under wings. The long, lancet-shaped tragus projects forward even when the ear is folded up. Eyes relatively large; muzzle bulbous at sides. Fur fluffy, long. Base of hairs dark grey-brown, on border to ventral side on side of neck often lighter, yellowish-brown spot. Ventral side light grey, sometimes with yellowish tinge. Lips light flesh colour, nose and eye area light brown, ears and wing membranes light grey-brown. Tragus yellowish-white, light grey pigmentation only towards tip. Juveniles pale grey without brown tones, dark face. Wings broad, lateral membrane starts at base of toes, calcar reaches approximately half length of tail membrane. Feet large, thumbs and thumb claws long; penis thin and narrowing towards end. Thumb > 6 (6.5–8.4) mm long, tragus width <5.5 (4.5–5.2) mm, foot 6.5–9.2 (11) mm.

Long-eared bat.

Colour anomalies Partial albinism (wing membranes and parts of ears).

Similar species Grey long-eared bat: base of hairs dark, slate grey, dorsal side appears altogether grey; nose, upper lip and tragus grey; note measurements of thumb, tragus and foot. Bechstein's bat: ears shorter, at base on front clearly separated.

Distribution Nearly all over Europe. In Scandinavia to about 64° N.; not recorded in southern Spain, southern Italy and Greece.

Status and protection Common and widespread in Great Britain. Britain's second commonest bat. Greatly endangered in West Germany due to timber treatment with chemicals. Specific roost and habitat protection, erection of bat boxes.

Habitat Fairly open deciduous and coniferous woodlands in

167

lowland and highlands, also in parks and gardens in villages and cities, but not dependent on human settlements. Highest nursery roost 1660 m (Switzerland) otherwise up to 2000 m, but usually below that. Summer roosts (nurseries) in tree holes, bat and bird boxes, in attics; individual animals also in rock caves, behind shutters, cracks in buildings. Winter roosts in buildings, cellars, mine tunnels, caves, very occasionally in well-insulated tree hollows. Temperature 2–5 °C, even down to −3.5 °C for 1–2 days; usually found nearer cave entrance than *Myotis* species due to its resistance to cold. In the roost wedged in cracks, also deep down in narrow pipes, sometimes hangs free from wall; wing membranes partially cover belly and chest. Usually solitary, very occasionally in small clusters (2–3 animals); may also occur mixed with other species. Hibernation from October/November until end of March/beginning of April.

Migration Sedentary species, usually only a few kilometres

Long-eared bat (left) and grey long-eared bat (right). The differences in fur and face colouring and in the length of thumbs and thumb claws can be seen very well. Both animals show resting posture in which they fold their ears back.

between summer and winter roost. Longest recorded movement 42 km.

Reproduction Females sexually mature in their second year. Mating season autumn (until spring?). Nursery roosts occupied in May/April, 10–50 (over 100) females. Males often found in nurseries. Nursery roosts in attics, not usually in one place but animals tend to be dispersed throughout the roof timbering or occupy crevices. Births from mid-June. One young, rarely two, eyes open on 4th day; ears are erected around 11th day; able to fly mid- to end of July. In autumn invasions of up to 10 animals in the living space of houses may occur (juveniles looking for roosts).

Maximum age 22 years. Average age 4.5 years.

Hunting and feeding Emergence in late dusk, but normally only when dark. Flight slow and fluttering, low, can hover, very agile in confined spaces. Preys on moths (mainly Noctuids), picks caterpillars, spiders and other prey off twigs and other surfaces and also catches butterflies in this manner (for example, peacock, small tortoiseshell). Prey may be eaten at feeding sites where remains of moth wings can be found. Observations of captive animals have suggested additional visual perception of prey as well as passive listening.

Calls In defence relatively deep chirping or humming; in spring and autumn call sequences in flight similar to 'tzick-tzick'.

Echolocation calls (searching flight) Sounds not usually detected in open areas in wild. Low, short FM signals from 83–26 kHz; duration 2 ms (see sonagram on page 212). Highest pulse intensities at 26, 42, 59 kHz; call sequence every 50 ms (20 signals per second). Short range, up to 2 m. Long-eared bats 'whisper', this is connected to their mode of hunting (hover or circle in front of leaves and twigs). Occasionally louder; 42–12 kHz; duration 7 ms; call sequence every 180–200 ms (5.4 signals per second).

Further illustrations Pages 35, 62, 199, 207, 209.

Grey long-eared bat

Plecotus austriacus (Fischer, 1829)

G Graues Langohr **F** Oreillard méridional

Head–body 41–58 (60) mm
Tail 37–55 (57) mm
Forearm (35) 37–45 mm
Ear 31–41 mm
Wingspan 255–300 mm
Condylobasal length 15–17 (17.2) mm
Weight 7–14 g

It was not until 1960 that this species was rediscovered in central Europe by Bauer.

Identification Medium-sized. Ears like long-eared bat, about 22–24 transverse folds, nose longer and more pointed; eyes relatively large. Fur long, base of hairs dark slate-grey. Dorsal side appears mainly grey, at most slight brownish tint. Ventral side light grey. Nose and upper lip dark grey/black, especially around eyes grey mask. Wing membranes and ears blackish; tragus pigmented grey from near base upwards. Wings broad, lateral membrane starts at base of toe, calcar nearly half length of tail membrane. Thumbs, thumb claws and feet small. Penis club-shaped at end. Thumb <6 mm; foot 6–8 mm; tragus width ≤5.5 mm.

Colour anomalies
Not known.

Similar species Long-eared bat, vague similarity also to Bechstein's bat (for characteristics see relevant section).

Distribution Central and S. Europe. In N. Europe: S. England, France, scattered records from Belgium and S. Netherlands; in West Germany, East Germany and Poland reaches about 53° N. Range does not extend to Baltic Sea coast. Common in Mediterranean and Balkan regions, Caucasus Mountains.

Status and protection Very rare in southern England. Much rarer than long-eared bat in central Europe. Protection of nursery roosts (wood preservation treatment with substances non-toxic to warm-blooded animals), protection of habitat.

Grey long-eared bat. Compared to most other European vesper bats, long-eared bats have relatively large eyes.

Grey long-eared bat in flight. The mouth is closed since long-eared bats emit echolocation calls through their nostrils.

Habitat Likes warmth. Prefers cultivated areas, in highlands in warm valleys usually below 400 m. In the north, usually associated with human settlements (house-dwelling bat), avoids larger woodlands. In summer recorded up to 1380 m, in winter up to 1100 m. Summer roosts (nurseries) in buildings, sometimes visible on ridge timbers, sometimes hidden away in cracks and cavities in beams; may be found in same roost as greater mouse-eared and lesser horseshoe bats. Winter roosts in caves, cellars, mine tunnels, may share with long-eared bat. Temperature 2–9 (12) °C. Hangs free from wall more frequently than long-eared bat but can also be found in crevices; usually solitary, rarely two or three animals together. Hibernation from September/October to March/April.

Migration Sedentary species, distance between summer and winter roosts below 20 km. Furthest known movement 62 km.

Reproduction Only fragmentary knowledge, small nursery roosts, usually 10–30 females, hang separately or in small groups hidden away in attics; so far no records of nursery roosts in tree hole or bat box. Births mid-/end of June. One young.

Maximum age 14.5 years.

Hunting and feeding Emerges in darkness. Flight like long-eared bat, very skilful. Often hunts in open spaces, also around street lights. Preys mainly on moths, diptera, small beetles. Has feeding perches.

Calls Chirping or humming calls when disturbed.

Further illustrations Pages 62, 168, 199, 207, 209.

Genus: *Barbastella* Gray, 1821

Two species, one of them in Europe.

Dental formula $\dfrac{2\ 1\ 2\ 3}{3\ 1\ 2\ 3} = 34$

Barbastelle
Barbastella barbastellus (Schreber, 1774)

G Mopsfledermaus   **F** Barbastelle

Head–body 45–58 mm
Tail (36) 38–52 mm
Forearm 36–44 mm
Ear 12–18 mm
Wingspan 260–290 mm
Condylobasal length 12–14.7 mm
Weight 6–13.5 g

Identification Medium-sized. Nose short, pug-shaped, nostrils opening upwards. Ear conches wide, opening faces forward; inner edges of ear joined together on top of head. Outer edge of ear with 5–6 transverse folds, roughly in the middle distinct knob-like skin flap that appears patched onto the ear but can also be absent (it is fully developed in only one-third of the animals in Czechoslovakia, but in over 90% of all animals in Poland, Lithuania and in East Germany). Tragus triangular with long rounded tip. Eyes small, gape of mouth very narrow, teeth small. Fur long, silky, base of hairs black. Dorsal side appears black-brown with whitish or yellowish-white tips and thus frosted. Ventral side dark-grey, naked parts of face and ears black, wing membranes grey-brown to black-brown. Wings narrow, long; lateral membrane starts at base of toes; calcar reaches approximately half length of tail membrane, tail membrane exceptionally large in area, very narrow post-calcarial lobe. One pair of mammary glands. Juveniles that can fly are somewhat darker but already possess whitish tips on their dorsal hair.

Colour anomalies Partial albinism occurs frequently (Czechoslovakia).

173

Similar species Cannot be confused in Europe. In the Caucasus Mountains, the very similar and slightly larger Asiatic species *Barbastella leucomelas* is supposed to occur sympatrically with *B. barbastellus* (*B. leucomelas*: forearm 41.2–45 mm, condylobasal length 14.2–14.9 mm). Contrary to the opinion of Kusjakin and other authors the absence of the skin flap on the outer ear-edge is not adequate to distinguish between the two species since this can also occur in *B. barbastellus*. Many authors doubt that *B. leucomelas* is a separate species and regard it merely as a sub-species of *B. barbastellus*.

Distribution Europe from England and Wales to Caucasus Mountains, in Norway and Sweden to about 60° N. Only small numbers in most areas; no records in southern Spain, most of Yugoslavia, Albania and Greece.

Status and protection Very rare throughout Great Britain no nursery roosts are known. Endangered or threatened with extinction over much of Europe. Causes of the often extreme decline in populations not precisely known, may be related to dramatic deterioration in available food sources owing to the use of insecticides. Specific habitat protection, particularly of known nursery roosts and hibernacula.

Habitat Prefers wooded foothills and mountainous regions, also areas of human settlement. Recorded in summer up to 1920 m (Col de Bretolet, Alps), highest nursery roost 1100 m (Czechoslovakia). Summer roosts (nurseries) in roof spaces, cracks in buildings, often behind shutters. Individual animals also in tree holes, nest boxes or in caves near the entrance. Hibernates in caves, mine tunnels, cellars, trees; cold-resistant species. Temperature 2–5 °C, in rare cases down to −3 °C or below. Can often be found near entrance of roost in severe weather. In narrow cracks as well as hanging free from wall or roof, sometimes in large clusters. Up to 1000 or more animals in large winter roosts (W. Poland), in many roosts a noticeable predominance of males. Hibernation from October/November to March/April.

Migration Occasional migrant. Longest recorded movements up to 300 km, but usually not as far.

Reproduction Females sexually mature in second year. Mating in autumn, also in hibernaculum. Nursery roosts often only 10–20 females, rarely up to 100. During this time males live in small groups apart from nurseries. Very sensitive to disturbance! Births from mid-June; usually single young, rarely two.

Maximum age 23 years.

Barbastelle. Small orange-coloured mite larvae often attach themselves tightly to the outer edge of the ear of this species.

Barbastelle.

Hunting and feeding Emergence in early dusk. Flight fast, skilful. Hunts low over water and at height of tree tops along woodland edges, in gardens and avenues. Preys on small, delicate insects (moths, diptera, small beetles), cannot manage larger insects with hard chitinous shell because of narrow gape and weak teeth.

Calls Rarely heard because it is a 'whispering' bat producing very weak sounds. High-pitched chirping and sometimes also dull humming if disturbed.

Echolocation calls (searching flight) Two call types (see sonagram on page 213): (a) Loud, short CF/FM signal at 35–28 kHz, duration 4 ms. (b) Low, short CF/FM signal at 43–33 kHz. Duration 5.2 ms. Both signals start with a CF component of 1–1.5 ms duration. Highest pulse intensity at 35–30 or 43 kHz; call sequence every 110–120 ms (8–9 signals per second).

Further illustrations Pages 19, 53, 67, 203, 207.

Genus: *Miniopterus* Bonaparte, 1837

Ten species, one in Europe.

Dental formula $\dfrac{2\ 1\ 2\ (3)\ 3}{3\ 1\ 3\quad 3} = 36\ (38)$

Schreiber's bat
Miniopterus schreibersii (Kuhl, 1819)

G Langflügelfledermaus   **F** Minioptère

Head–body (48) 50–62 mm
Tail (47) 56–64 mm
Forearm (44) 45–48 mm
Ear 10–13.5 mm
Wingspan 305–342 mm
Condylobasal length 14.5–15.5 mm
Weight 9–16 g

Identification Medium-sized. Very short nose, domed forehead, ears short, triangular, very far apart, do not project above top of head, 4–5 transverse folds; tragus short, bent inwards, rounded at tip. Dorsal fur short. Fur on head short, dense, standing erect; dorsal side grey-brown to ash-grey, sometimes with slight lilac tinge. Ventral side somewhat lighter grey. Adult animals in Romania and Bulgaria have a distinctly defined yellow- to cinnamon-brown throat patch, as well as similarly coloured hairs on their foreheads; this colouring is altogether missing in the greyer juveniles (without brown tones). Nose, ears and wing membranes grey-brown, tragus yellowish-white, sometimes with light-grey pigment. Wings long and narrow, 2nd phalanx of 3rd finger about three times as long as 1st phalanx; at rest 3rd and 4th finger are bent inwards at the joint between 1st and 2nd phalanx; this position is usually maintained even in passively spread wings (the other vesper bats bend all phalanges of the 3rd to 5th fingers at the joint between the metacarpals and the phalanges when the wing is folded). Lateral membrane starts at heel. Feet and tail relatively long, calcar reaches about one-third to half of tail membrane length, no post-calcarial lobe. Very calm in behaviour.

Colour anomalies Albinism.

Similar species Unmistakable in Europe.

Distribution Southern and S.E. Europe; in the north as far as Spain, France, Switzerland, Austria, Czechoslovakia (Slovakia), Hungary; widespread in Mediterranean and Balkan regions; Caucasus Mountains.

Status and protection Obviously very sensitive species; large colonies have become extinct in France and Switzerland. In West Germany classified as endangered breeding vagrant; threatened with extinction in Austria. Specific roost protection required.

Habitat Cave-dwelling bat; found in lowlands as well as in mountains (up to 1000 m), limestone areas. Summer roosts (nurseries) in caves, in the north of their range occasionally in large attics. Hibernates in caves. Temperature 7–12 °C, hangs free from wall or roof, sometimes in clusters, hibernacula may be changed even in winter. Hibernation from October (?) until end of March.

Migration Migratory species at least in the north. Hibernacula as much as 100 km or more further south than summer roosts. Longest recorded movement 350 km.

Reproduction Females sexually mature in their second year. Mating in autumn; in contrast to all other European bats fertilization takes place immediately but embryonic development is suspended during hibernation and resumes again in spring (delayed implantation), gestation period therefore 8–9 months. Nursery roosts often over 1000 females; males also frequently present in nurseries. Births end of June/beginning of July. One young, very occasionally two.

Maximum age   16 years.

Schreiber's bat.

Hunting and feeding Emergence shortly after sunset. Flight very fast (50–55 km/h), reminiscent of swallow or swift flight. Hunts at 10–20 m height above ground in open areas, often at a long distance from the roost. Preys on moths, gnats and beetles.

Calls Shrill, short scolding when disturbed; at rest within a group deep whispering similar to isolation calls made by small goose or duck chicks.

Further illustrations Pages 199, 207.

Schreiber's bat. In this adult animal from the Rodopi Mountains (Bulgaria), note the cinnamon-brown throat patch and the lighter tragus (subspecies: *Miniopterus schreibersii inexpectatus*).

Family Free-tailed bats (*Molossidae*)
Genus: *Tadarida* Rafinesque, 1814

52 species, one in Europe.

Dental formula $\dfrac{1\ 1\ 2\ 3}{3\ 1\ 2\ 3} = 32$

European free-tailed bat
Tadarida teniotis (Rafinesque, 1814)

G Europäische Bulldoggfledermaus **F** Molosse de Cestoni

Head–body 81–92 mm
Tail 44–57 mm
Forearm 57–64 mm
Ear 27–31 mm
Wingspan c. 410 mm
Condylobasal length 20.9–24 mm
Weight 25–50 g

Identification Very large. Ears long, broad, project forwards beyond eyes and face, the base of the two ears touching at the front; outer edge of ears wider at approximately eye-height, with an obvious, almost rectangular, skin flap (anti-tragus). Muzzle long, upper lip with five folds, nostril opening towards front, eyes large. Fur short, fine, soft, almost mole-like. Dorsal side black-grey to smokey grey, with brownish sheen. Ventral side somewhat lighter grey. Ears, nose and wing membranes black-grey. Juveniles greyer. Tail membrane short, one-third to half of the tail protrudes beyond the membrane, calcar without post-calcarial lobe. Wings very narrow, long; lateral membrane starts at heel. Animals smell intensely of a mixture of musk and lavender. Can walk well and climb in cracks. Legs short and strong.

Colour anomalies Not known.

Similar species Unmistakable in Europe.

Distribution Southern Europe, Mediterranean region, records (often only solitary animals) from Portugal, Spain, southern France, Switzerland, Italy, Yugoslavia, Albania, Bulgaria, Greece, Mediterranean islands.

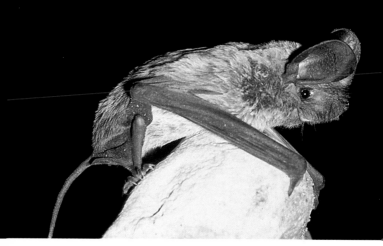

Status and protection No specific advice possible since very little is known about the life cycle and habits of this species.

Habitat Rock-dwelling bat, in mountains with steep cliffs and gorges as well as in areas of human settlement. Recorded up to 1920 m (Col de Bretolet, Alps). Summer roosts in rock crevices, on Mediterranean islands also in crevices of sea cliffs, cave roofs, crevices on buildings. Hibernation sites not known. No precise information is available on whether this species hibernates for long periods of time.

Migration Probably migratory or occasional migrant.

Reproduction Knowledge insufficient. Females probably sexually mature in first year. One young, independent after 6–7 weeks.

Maximum age Not precisely known, but over 10 years.

Hunting and feeding Emergence sometimes in early dusk, but usually later. Flight high, fast and straight; needs wide open air space. May also hunt circling over water. Preys on flying insects.

Calls In flight loud, sharp 'tsick', also whistling signals.

Echolocation calls (searching flight) CF signals, largely long CF signal of c. 20 ms duration, slight drop in frequency from 18–10 kHz (see sonagram on page 213). Call sequence appears to vary (1–4 signals per second).

Further illustrations Pages 24, 199.

Identification key to European bats

The key is based on the external features of live adult bats and enables the user to identify all European species, separated according to families. The only aids required are a magnifying glass and a ruler (or callipers). Additional help is given by referring to the illustrations included in the text. The sequence of features roughly corresponds to their degree of reliability when used for identification. Juvenile bats (note unfused epiphyses in animals less than 45 days old, see drawing) are usually duller and darker in colour. If in doubt identification should be carried out by an expert.

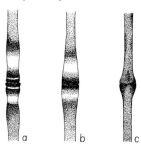

Degree of ossification of the epiphyses of metacarpals and phalanges of **a.** young bats, **b.** juvenile bats, and **c.** adult bats (based on Gromov, 1963).

Identification of the families

A – Nose with skin appendages (horseshoe, sella, lancet; Figure 1); ear without tragus (Figures 2a, b).
Horseshoe bat family (Rhinolophidae). 187

B – Nose without appendages; ear with tragus (e.g. Figure 3); tail enclosed in tail membrane completely or except for the last 2 vertebrae (c. 4–9 mm; e.g. Figure 5).
Vesper bat family (Vespertilionidae). 188

C – Tail projects from tail membrane by one-third to one-half; lower outer edge of ear (anti-tragus) with noticeable flap formations (Figure 2i); no nose appendages.
Free-tailed bat family (Molossidae). 193

A. Horseshoe bats

1a – Upper connecting process blunt in profile
(Figures 1b, d). 2
1b – Upper connecting process pointed in profile and always
longer than lower connecting process
(Figures 1f, h, j). 3

2a – Forearm longer than 50 mm, nose leaf (Figure 1a, b).
Greater horseshoe bat (*Rhinolophus ferrumequinum*), p.92
2b – Forearm shorter than 43 mm, nose leaf (Figure 1c, d).
Lesser horseshoe bat (*Rhinolophus hipposideros*), p.88

3a – 2nd phalanx of 4th finger more than twice as long as first
(Figure 6k);
lower connecting process broad, rounded when seen from
front;
transverse fold below lancet without central notch when
seen from front (Figures 1e, g). 4
3b – 2nd phalanx of 4th finger at most twice as long as first;
lower connecting process narrow, rounded when seen from
front;
transverse fold below lancet slightly notched in the centre
when seen from front (Figure 1i);
lancet tapering more or less evenly towards top (Figure 1i);
sella in profile (Figure 1j).
Blasius's horseshoe bat (*Rhinolophus blasii*), p.98

4a – Lancet tapering more or less evenly towards top
(Figure 1e);
upper connecting process pointed in profile, bent forwards,
distinctly longer than lower connecting process
(Figure 1f).
Mediterranean horseshoe bat (*Rhinolophus euryale*), p.95
4b – Sudden narrowing of lancet from middle upwards, tapering
to thin point (Figure 1g);
upper connecting process relatively blunt in profile and
only slightly longer than lower connecting process
(Figure 1h);
often some conspicuous dark hairs in eye region ('spectacles').
Mehely's horseshoe bat (*Rhinolophus mehelyi*), p. 100

B. Vesper bats

1a – Ears joined together at base by a fold of skin (Figures 2g, 4i);
nostrils open upwards (Figures 2g, h; 4h, i).
Genera *Barbastella* and *Plecotus*. 2
1b – Ears widely separated (e.g. Figure 3);
nostrils open forwards (e.g. Figure 3).
Genera *Myotis, Miniopterus, Eptesicus, Pipistrellus, Nyctalus, Vespertilio*. 4

2a – Ears longer than 30 mm, many transverse folds, folded when at rest. . . . 3
2b – Ears short and broad (Figures 4h, i);
dorsal fur black-brown with light tips, frosted effect;
calcar with small post-calcarial lobe (Figure 6a).
Barbastelle bat (*Barbastella barbastellus*), p.173

3a – Tragus with grey pigment almost from the base upwards, more than 5.5 mm wide (Figure 2h);
thumb under 6 mm, thumb claw short, c. 2 mm (Figure 7h);
face with dark mask including eyes, facial skin with grey pigment (Figure 2h);
dorsal fur predominantly grey, back hairs dark slate-grey at base; ventral side grey-white, without brownish tinge; penis club-shaped at end (Figure 7d).
Grey long-eared bat (*Plecotus austriacus*), p.170
3b – Tragus pale, with slight pigmentation towards tip, less than 5.5 mm wide (Figure 2g);
thumb over 6 mm, claw long and pointed, 2.5–3 mm (Figure 7g);
facial skin brownish flesh-coloured, dark pigment patch only on eyes, no dark mask (Figure 2g);
dorsal fur greyer-brown, dorsal hairs with dark-brown base, ventral side grey-white with brownish tinge. No club-shaped end to penis (Figure 7c).
Long-eared bat (*Plecotus auritus*), p.166

4a – Calcar with post-calcarial lobe (e.g. Figure 6c);
tragus short, curved, rounded at tip (e.g. Figure 4a) or mushroom-shaped (e.g. Figure 2e).
Genera *Nyctalus, Pipistrellus, Eptesicus, Vespertilio*. 5
4b – Calcar without post-calcarial lobe (e.g. Figure 5e); if narrow keel present (Figure 5c) then tragus lancet-shaped, reaching about half ear-length (e.g. Figure 3g).
Genera *Myotis, Miniopterus*. 14

5a – Last tail vertebra projects beyond membrane max. 1 mm (Figure 5g);
post-calcarial lobe broad with visible T-piece cartilage. 9

5b – Last 1–2 tail vertebrae project beyond membrane 4–5 mm;
post-calcarial lobe narrow, usually without visible T-piece cartilage (Figure 6b). 6

6a – Forearm over 47 mm;
dorsal fur dark brown, sometimes glossy but without gold sheen, ventral side yellowish-brown, no distinct border between dorsal and ventral side;
post-calcarial lobe narrow, without visible T-piece cartilage, tail membrane (Figure 6b), ear with narrow outer edge which ends before the corner of the mouth (Figure 4f).
Serotine bat (*Eptesicus serotinus*), p.143

6b – Forearm max. 47 mm;
dorsal fur of adult animals with light-yellow or white tips. 7

7a – Outer edge of ear with broad fold running under the line of the mouth and then rising to end at the corner of the mouth (Figure 4g);
post-calcarial lobe wide, with visible T-piece cartilage;
dorsal hairs dark-brown at base, appears frosted owing to whitish hair tips, ventral side whitish with distinct border between dorsal and ventral side;
females have 4 mammary glands;
forearm 40–47 mm.
Parti-coloured bat (*Vespertilio murinus*), p.150

7b – Outer edge of ear with narrow fold leading towards and ending just before the corner of the mouth (Figures 4d, e);
post-calcarial lobe without visible T-piece cartilage;
dorsal hairs dark-brown at base, tips yellowish or with gold sheen. 8

8a – Tragus distinctly longer than it is wide, slightly bent (Figure 4e);
narrow post-calcarial lobe;
dorsal fur with gold sheen, ventral side yellowish-brown, distinct border to dorsal side only on throat;
forearm 38–44 mm.
Northern bat (*Eptesicus nilssonii*), p.147

8b – Tragus short, widens slightly towards top (Figure 4d), length of its front edge is roughly equal to its largest width, on the base of the outer edge two little serrations one above the other;
ears and face black, contrasts strongly with the light

brownish-yellow tips of dorsal fur and the almost white ventral side;
forearm 30–38 mm.
Savi's pipistrelle bat (*Pipistrellus savii*), p.163

9a – Tragus mushroom-like towards top (Figures 2d, e, f);
forearm over 38 mm. 12
9b – Tragus not mushroom-like towards top;
forearm under 38 mm. 10

10a – Teeth: I^1 usually with one point, I^2 very small, P^1 not visible from outside, displaced inwards (see Figure on p.154);
clearly delimited white strip, c. 2 mm wide, on edge of wing membrane between 5th finger and leg (note: dark grey-brown animals without white membrane edge sometimes occur!);
ears brown (Figure 4c).
Kuhl's pipistrelle bat (*Pipistrellus kuhli*), p.161
10b – I^1 two points (Figures a & b, p.154);
wing membrane without white edge or only slightly lighter;
ears blackish (Figures 4a, b). 11

11a – Forearm 32–37 mm;
5th finger over 42 mm (females) or 41 mm (males);
P^1 well developed, visible from outside, I^2 longer than the short tip of I^1 (Figure b on p.154);
tail membrane covered with hairs to middle dorsal side (Figure 5k), ear (Figure 4a);
ventral side covered with hairs only along lower leg.
Nathusius' pipistrelle bat (*Pipistrellus nathusii*), p.158
11b – Forearm 28–34.6 mm;
5th finger up to 42 mm (females) or 41 mm (males);
P^1 small, displaced inwards, hardly visible from outside, I^2 shorter than small tip of I^1 (Figure a on p.154);
lack of hair on lower leg and tail membrane (Figure 5h), and ear (Figure 4b).
Pipistrelle bat (*Pipistrellus pipistrellus*), p.153

12a – Dorsal fur brown, hairs of two colours, darker at base, lighter tips;
forearm 39–46 mm, ear (Figure 2f).
Leisler's bat (*Nyctalus leisleri*), p.138
12b – Dorsal fur rufous brown, hairs of one colour. 13

13a – Forearm 48–58 mm, ear (Figure 2e).
Noctule (*Nyctalus noctula*), p.134
13b – Forearm 63–69 mm, ear (Figure 2d).
Greater noctule bat (*Nyctalus lasiopterus*), p.141

14a – Very small, triangular ears which do not project above the top of the head (Figure 2c);
hair on head short, standing erect, distinct border with smooth fur on back;
3rd and 4th fingers are bent at the joint between 1st and 2nd phalanx when at rest (Figure 6j);
2nd phalanx of 3rd finger about three times as long as 1st.
Schreiber's bat (*Miniopterus schreibersii*), p.177

14b – Ears always longer than broad, project over top of head (Figure 3);
tragus lancet-shaped, more or less tapering to a point (Figure 3).
Genera *Myotis*. 15

15a – Forearm over 50 mm. 16
15b – Forearm under 50 mm. 17

16a – Ear over 26 mm, front edge bent backwards, tip of ear relatively wide (Figure 3a);
nose long, relatively broad at front;
forearm 54–67 mm.
Greater mouse-eared bat (*Myotis myotis*), p.129

16b – Ear under 26 mm, front edge relatively straight, ear narrower and pointed towards tip (Figure 3b);
nose relatively short and pointed;
forearm 52–61.5 mm.
Lesser mouse-eared bat (*Myotis blythi*), p.132

17a – Ear over 20 mm (Figure 3c), nearly half of its length projects beyond tip of nose if ear is bent forward;
calcar straight, with narrow keel, less than half length of the tail membrane edge, last tail vertebra free (Figure 5i);
forearm 39–47 mm.
Bechstein's bat (*Myotis bechsteinii*), p.126

17b – Ear under 20 mm, if bent forwards does not project more than 5 mm beyond tip of nose. 18

18a – S-shaped calcar, roughly half as long as tail membrane edge, free edge of tail membrane wrinkled and densely covered with short, curved bristles (Figure 5f);
tragus long, lightly coloured, lancet-shaped, larger than half ear length (Figure 3f).
Natterer's bat (*Myotis nattereri*), p.123

18b – Calcar straight or slightly curved only on one side (Figure e.g. 5c). 19

19a – Calcar is about one-third length of tail membrane edge, two-thirds to three-quarters along length of the latter there is a distinct flap which appears like the calcar end (Figures

5d, e, n);

feet with long bristles;

outer ear edge without distinct indentation (e.g. Figure 3e). 20

19b – Maximum length of calcar half length tail membrane edge, no flap two-thirds to three-quarters along length of tail membrane edge (Figures 5c, b);

outer edge of ear with distinct indentation (Figures 3g, h, i). 22

20a – Lateral membrane starts above ankle (Figure 5o);

tail membrane on top and underneath covered with dark downy hairs from the legs to roughly the middle of the membrane (near calcar end; Figure 5n, o);

dorsal fur grey;

tragus slightly S-shaped, reaches at least half ear length (Figure 5m);

forearm 38–44 mm.

Long-fingered bat (*Myotis capaccinii*), p.108

20b – Lateral membrane starts at heel or in the middle of the sole of the foot (Figure 5d, e);

tail membrane without obvious hairs on upper side;

tragus straight, does not reach half ear length (Figures 3d, e);

dorsal fur brownish, glossy. 21

21a – Forearm 43–49 mm;

tragus distinctly shorter than half ear length (Figure 3d);

fine whitish hairs underneath tail membrane along lower leg up to calcar (Figure 5d);

lateral membrane starts at heel.

Pond bat (*Myotis dasycneme*), p.110

21b – Forearm 33–42 mm;

tragus reaches nearly half ear length (Figure 3e);

tail membrane without hairs;

lateral membrane starts at base of 1st toe (Figure 5e).

Daubenton's bat (*Myotis daubentonii*), p.104

22a – Tragus does not reach notch in outer edge of ear (Figure 3i);

dorsal fur long, woolly, with reddish sheen;

calcar without keel (Figure 5l).

Geoffroy's bat (*Myotis emarginatus*), p.120

22b – Tragus projects over notch in outer edge of ear (Figures 3g, h);

fur dark grey-brown or yellowish-brown with gold sheen;

calcar with narrow keel (Figure 5c). 23

23a – Penis club-shaped at end (Figure 7a);

ears, face and wing membranes brownish, base of inner edge of ear and tragus light flesh colour (Figure 3g);

dorsal fur in adult animals usually light brown with gold sheen;

cusp in P^3 higher than or same height as P^2 (Figure p.119, left);

P_2 not distinctly smaller than P_1 (Figure p.119);

forearm 33–39 mm.

Brandt's bat (*Myotis brandtii*), p.119

23b – Penis not club-shaped (Figure 7b);

ears, face and flight membrane blackish, no lighter base to inner edge of ear (Figure 3h);

dorsal fur predominantly grey-brown to black-brown;

cusp in P^3 lower than P^2, P_2 distinctly smaller than P_1 (Figure p.119, right);

forearm 31–38 mm.

Whiskered bat (*Myotis mystacinus*), p.116

C. Free-tailed bats

Only one species in Europe, **European free-tailed bat** (*Tadarida teniotis*), ear shown in Figure 2i.

Important body measurements

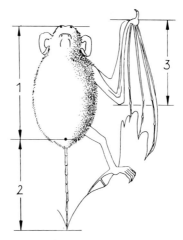

1. Body length

2. Tail length

3. Forearm length

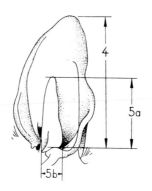

4. Ear length

5a. Tragus length

5b. Tragus width

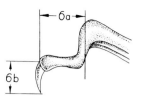

6a. Thumb length

6b. Thumb-claw length

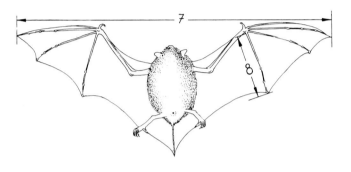

7. Wingspan

8. Length of 5th finger
(more correctly, length of 5th metacarpal and of 5th finger)

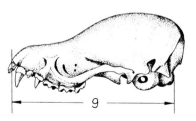

9. Condylobasal length

Figure I

Nose leaves of European horseshoe bats

a, b Greater horseshoe bat

c, d. Lesser horseshoe bat

e, f. Mediterranean horseshoe bat

g, h. Mehely's horseshoe bat

i, j. Blasius' horseshoe bat

(Photographs **a–h** E. Grimmberger,
i, j H. Hackethal)

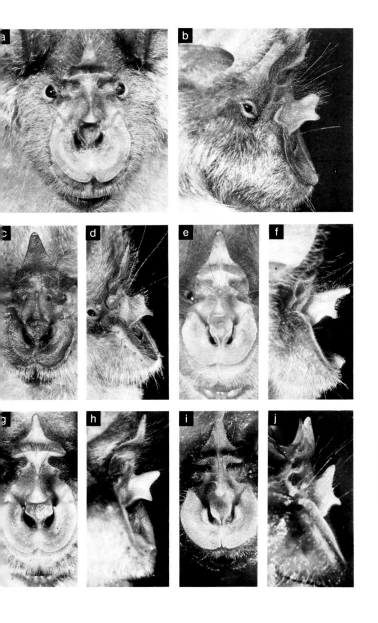

Figure 2

Ear shapes

a. Mediterranean horseshoe bat

b. Mehely's horseshoe bat

c. Schreiber's bat

d. Greater noctule bat

e. Noctule bat

f. Leisler's bat

g. Long-eared bat

h. Grey long-eared bat

i. European free-tailed bat

(Photographs **a–c, e–h** E. Grimmberger,
d O. v. Helversen, **i** J. Cervany)

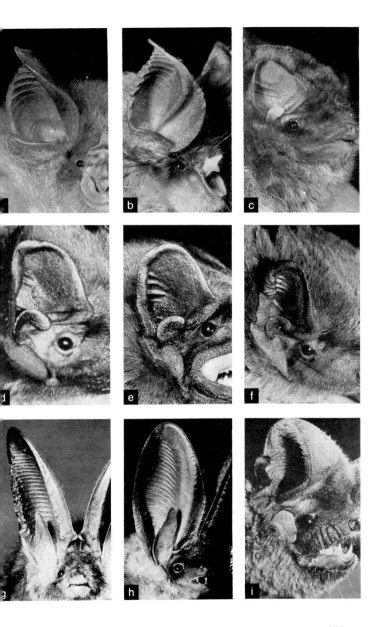

Figure 3

Ear shapes

a. Greater mouse-eared bat

b. Lesser mouse-eared bat

c. Bechstein's bat

d. Pond bat

e. Daubenton's bat

f. Natterer's bat

g. Brandt's bat

h. Whiskered bat

i. Geoffroy's bat

(Photographs **a** H. Hackethal,
b–i E. Grimmberger)

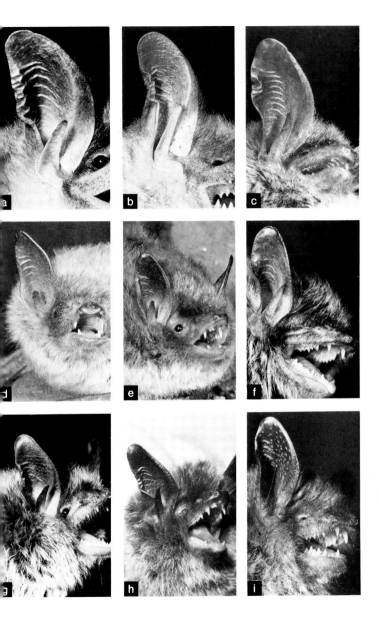

Figure 4

Ear shapes

a. Nathusius' pipistrelle bat

b. Pipistrelle bat

c. Kuhl's pipistrelle bat

d. Savi's pipistrelle bat

e. Northern bat

f. Serotine

g. Parti-coloured bat

h. Barbastelle (with ear flap)

i. Barbastelle (without ear flap)

(Photographs **a–b, e–i** E. Grimmberger,
c–d J. Gebhard)

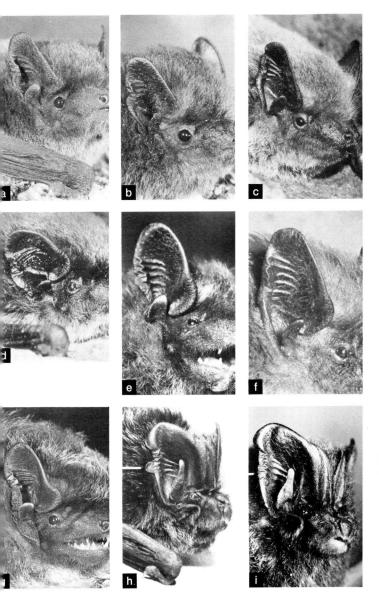

Figure 5

Tail membranes

The line points to the end of the calcar (in **d** and **e** to the flap in the tail membrane).

a. Greater mouse-eared bat

b. Lesser mouse-eared bat

c. Brandt's bat

d. Pond bat

e. Daubenton's bat

f. Natterer's bat

g. Pipistrelle (ventral side)

h. Pipistrelle (dorsal side, line shows limit of fur)

i. Bechstein's bat

j. Nathusius' pipistrelle bat (ventral side)

k. Nathusius' pipistrelle bat (dorsal side, line shows limit of fur)

l. Geoffroy's bat

m. Long-fingered bat, ear

n. Long-fingered bat, dorsal

o. Long-fingered bat, ventral

(photographs by E. Grimmberger)

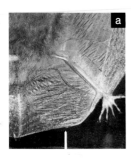
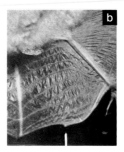
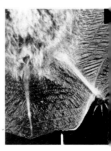

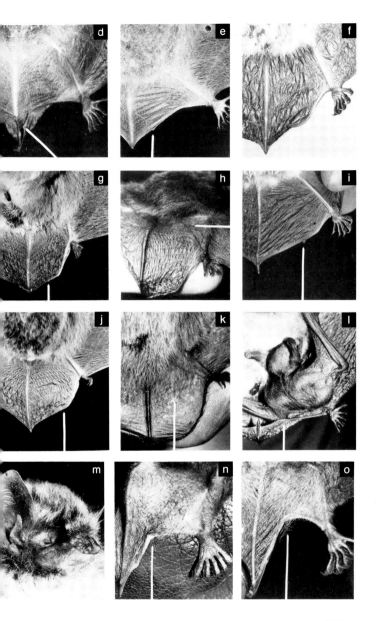

Figure 6

Tail membranes and wings

a. Barbastelle bat

b. Serotine

c. Noctule bat

d. Long-eared bat

e. Grey long-eared bat

f. Schreiber's bat (line shows where calcar ends)

g. Mediterranean horseshoe bat, sleeping position, 3rd to 5th fingers are bent in first finger joint (line shows 1st joint of 3rd finger)

h. Lesser horseshoe bat, sleeping position (line shows 1st joint of 3rd finger)

i. Natterer's bat, 3rd to 5th fingers are bent at joint between phalanges and metacarpals (here not completely; line shows joint of 3rd finger)

j. Schreiber's bat, only the 3rd to 5th fingers are at the 1st finger joint (line shows 1st phalanx, 4th finger)

k. Mediterranean horseshoe bat, bending of the fingers (line shows 1st phalanx of the 4th finger)

(Photographs by E. Grimmberger)

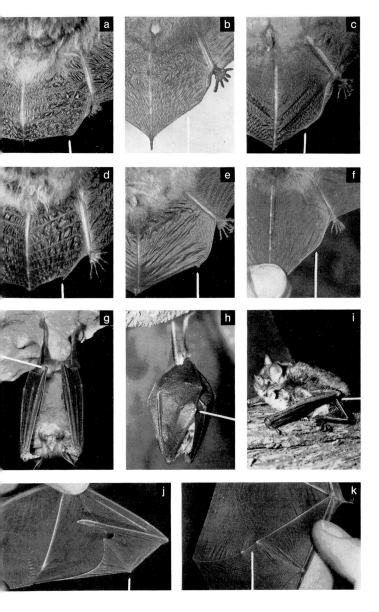

Figure 7

a. Penis, Brandt's bat

b. Penis, whiskered bat

c. Penis, long-eared bat

d. Penis, grey long-eared bat

e. Penis, Nathusius' pipistrelle, during the mating season the testes and epididymis (arrowed) are enlarged and clearly visible

f. Penis, noctule bat

g. Thumb, long-eared bat

h. Thumb, grey long-eared bat

i. False nipples (arrowed), greater horseshoe bat, adult female (left line shows mammary gland, right line shows false nipple)

j. Nipple of lactating female Brandt's bat, top left start of the lateral membrane, top right part of the ear is visible

k. Two-day-old pipistrelle bat suckling (to show this the mother's wing is lifted)

(Photographs E. Grimmberger)

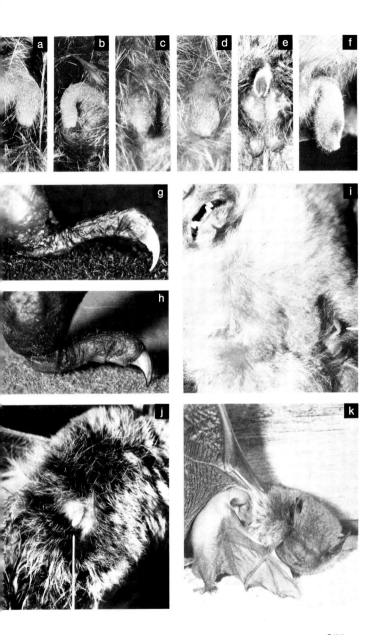

Sonagrams

(after Heller and Weid)

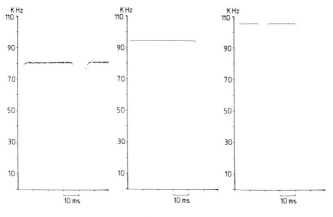

Greater horseshoe bat

Mediterranean
horseshoe bat

Blasius's horseshoe bat

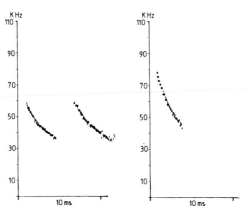

Bechstein's bat
(two different types of call)

Sonagrams

(after Ahlén)

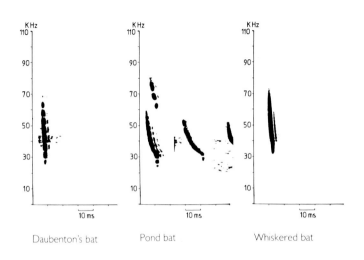

Daubenton's bat   Pond bat   Whiskered bat

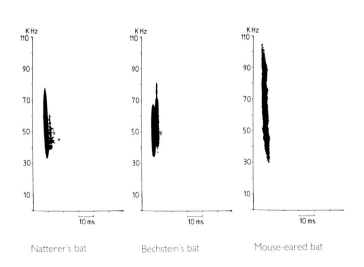

Natterer's bat   Bechstein's bat   Mouse-eared bat

Sonagrams

(after Ahlén)

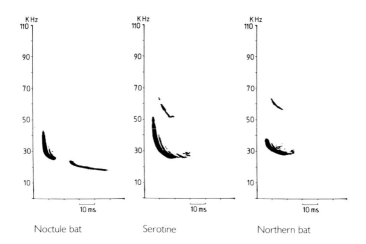

Noctule bat   Serotine   Northern bat

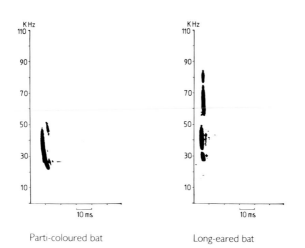

Parti-coloured bat   Long-eared bat

Sonagrams

(after Ahlén and Weid)

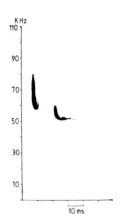

Pipistrelle bat

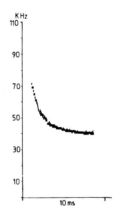

Nathusius' pipistrelle bat

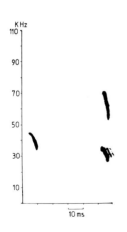

Barbastelle bat

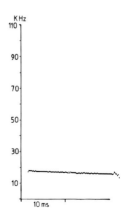

European free-tailed bat

Table 1
European bats at a glance

Species	Nursery sites	Movement
Lesser horseshoe bat	caves (buildings)	sedentary
Greater horseshoe bat	caves (buildings)	sedentary
Mediterranean horseshoe bat	caves (buildings)	sedentary
Blasius's horseshoe bat	caves	sedentary
Mehely's horseshoe bat	caves	sedentary
Daubenton's bat	trees (buildings)	occasional migrant
Long-fingered bat	caves	?
Pond bat	buildings	occasional migrant
Brandt's bat	trees (buildings)	occasional migrant (?)
Whiskered bat	buildings (trees)	sedentary (?)
Geoffroy's bat	buildings (caves)	sedentary
Natterer's bat	trees (buildings)	sedentary
Bechstein's bat	trees	sedentary
Greater mouse-eared bat	buildings (caves)	occasional migrant
Lesser mouse-eared bat	caves (buildings)	occasional migrant
Noctule	trees (buildings)	migratory
Leisler's bat	trees (buildings)	migratory
Greater noctule	trees	migratory (?)
Serotine	buildings	sedentary
Northern bat	buildings	sedentary (?)
Parti-coloured bat	rock crevices (buildings)	migratory
Pipistrelle	buildings (trees)	sedentary
Nathusius' pipistrelle	trees	migratory
Kuhl's pipistrelle	buildings (rock crevices)	sedentary (?)
Savi's pipistrelle	buildings (rock crevices?)	occasional migrant
Long-eared bat	trees (buildings)	sedentary
Grey long-eared bat	buildings	sedentary
Barbastelle	trees (buildings)	occasional migrant
Schreiber's bat	caves	migratory
European free-tailed bat	rock crevices	occasional migrant

Biological and ecological data

Preferred temperature in hibernaculum	Number of young	Maximum recorded age
6–9°C	1	21 years
7–11°C	1	30 years
c.10°C	1	?
?	1	?
?	1	?
(−2)3–8°C	1	22 years
?	1	?
0.5–7.5°C	1	19 years 6 months
(0)3–7.5°C	1	19 years 8 months
2–8°C	1	19 years
6–9°C	1	16 years
(−0.5)2.8–8°C	1	17 years 6 months
3–7°C	1	21 years
3–12°C	1	22 years
6–12°C	1	13 years
0°C–?	1 (2–3)	12 years
?	1 (2)	9 years
?	1 (2)	?
2–4°C	1 (2–3)	19 years 3 months
1–5.5°C	2	14 years 6 months
?	2 (1)	5 years
2–6°C	1 (2)	16 years 7 months
?	1 (2)	7 years
?	1 (2)	8 years
?	1 (2)	?
2–5°C	1 (1–2)	22 years
2–9°C	1	14 years 7 months
(−3)2–5°C	1 (2)	23 years
7–12°C	1	16 years
?	1	over 10 years

Table 2
Chiroptera of the world: systematics, distribution and diet

Systematics

Suborder Megachiroptera	
Family Pteropodidae	Flying foxes
Suborder Microchiroptera	
Superfamily Emballonuroidea	
Family Rhinopomatidae	Mouse-tailed bats
Family Craseonycteridae	Hog-faced bats
Family Emballonuridae	Sheath-tailed bats
Family Noctilionidae	Fisherman bats
Superfamily Rhinolophoidea	
Family Nycteridae	Slit-faced bats
Family Megadermatidae	False vampires
Family Rhinolophidae*	Horseshoe bats
Family Hipposideridae	Old World Leaf-nosed bats
Superfamily Phyllostomoidea	
Family Phyllostomidae	Spear-nosed bats
Family Mormoopidae	Moustached, ghost-faced bats

*Families with species occurring in Europe

Number of species	Distribution	Diet
175	only Old World, tropics and subtropics from Africa to Australia and Pacific	fruit, blossoms, pollen
3	North Africa, Asia to Sumatra	insects
1	South-east Asia (Thailand)	insects
50	World-wide (pantropical)	insects
2	Central and South America (tropics)	fish, insects
12	Africa, East Asia	insects
5	Africa, Asia, Australia (tropics)	insects, small vertebrates
70	Old World	insects
60	Africa, Asia, Australia (tropics)	insects
148	S. and western USA, Central and South America	insects, small vertebrates, fruit, pollen, blood
8	S. and western USA, Central and South America	insects

Systematics

Superfamily Vespertilionidea	
Family Vespertilionidae*	Vesper bats, evening bats
Family Natalidae	Funnel-eared bats
Family Furipteridae	Smokey bats
Family Thyropteridae	Disk-winged bats
Family Myzopodidae	Old World Sucker-footed bats
Family Mystacinidae	Short-tailed bats
Family Molossidae*	Free-tailed bats

* Families with species occurring in Europe.

Number of species	Distribution	Diet
320	world-wide (Nearctic, Palaearctic, South Africa, Australia, South America, W. Pacific, Hawaii, New Zealand	insects, fish, small vertebrates
6	Central America, Caribbean	insects
2	Central America, tropical South America	insects
2	Central America, tropical South America	insects
1	Madagascar	insects
2	New Zealand	insects
90	world-wide (mostly pan-tropical, also Southern Europe and in southern North America)	insects

Bibliography

AHLEN, I.: Identification of Scandinavian bats by their sounds. Swed. Univ. Agric. Sci., Dept. of Wildlife Ecology, Report 6, Uppsala 1981

ANDĚRA, M. & HORÁČEK, I.: Poznáváme naše savce (Wir bestimmen unsere Säugetiere). Mladá Fronta, Praha 1982

BAUER, K. & SPITZENBERGER, F.: Rote Liste seltener und gefährdeter Säugetierarten Österreichs (Mammalia). In: Rote Listen gefährdeter Tiere Österreichs. Bundesministerium für Gesundheit und Umweltschutz, Wien 1983

BAUMANN, F.: Die freilebenden Säugetiere der Schweiz. Bern 1949

BLAB, J.: Grundlagen für ein Fledermaus-Hilfsprogramm. Themen der Zeit, 5, Kilda-Verlag, Greven 1980

BLAB, J., NOWAK, E., TRAUTMANN, W. & SUKOPP, H.: Rote Listen der gefährdeten Tiere und Pflanzen in der Bundesrepublik Deutschland. Naturschutz aktuell Nr. 1; 4th edition, Kilda-Verlag, Greven 1984

BRINK, F. H. VAN DEN: Die Säugetiere Europas. Verl. P. Parey, Hamburg & Berlin 1975

BROSSET, A.: La Biologie des Chiropteres. Másson et Cie., Paris 1966

ČERVENÝ, J.: Abnormal Coloration in Bats (Chiroptera) of Czechoslovakia. Nyctalus (N.F.) 1, 193–202 (1980)

CORBET, G. & OVENDEN, D.: Pareys Buch der Säugetiere. Alle wildlebenden Säugetiere Europas. Verl. P. Parey, Hamburg & Berlin 1982

DEBLASE, A.F.: The bats of Iran: Systematics, Distribution, Ecology. Fieldiana Zoology, New Series No. 4, Chicago 1980

EISENTRAUT, M.: Die Fledertiere. In: Grzimeks Tierleben, Bd. 11. Kindler Verlag, Zürich 1969

GAISLER, J.: Ecology of bats. In: Stoddart, M. (Ed.) Ecology of small mammals. Chapman and Hall Ltd., London 1979

GEBHARD, J.: Unsere Fledermäuse. 2nd edition, Naturhistor. Museum Basel 1985

GRIMMBERGER, E. & BORK, H.: Untersuchungen zur Biologie, Ökologie und Populationsdynamik der Zwergfledermaus, *Pipistrellus p. pipistrellus* (Schreber 1774) in einer großen Population im Norden der DDR. Nyctalus (N.F.) 1, 55–73 & 122–136 (1978)

HACKETHAL, H.: Zur Merkmalsvariabilität mitteleuropäischer Bartfledermäuse unter besonderer Berücksichtigung der Verbreitung und der ökologischen Ansprüche von *Myotis brandti* (Eversmann 1845). Nyctalus (N.F.) 1, 293–410 (1982)

HACKETHAL, H.: Fledermäuse. In: Stresemann. Exkursionsfauna, Bd. 3 Wirbeltiere. Volk und Wissen VE Verlag, Berlin 1983

HAENSEL, J. & NÄFE, M.: Anleitungen zum Bau von Fledermauskästen und bisherige Erfahrungen mit ihrem Einsatz. Nyctalus (N.F.) **1,** 327–348 (1982)

HANÁK, V. & HORÁČEK, I.: Some comments of the taxonomy of *Myotis daubentoni* (Kuhl, 1819) (Chiroptera, Mammalia). Myotis **21–22,** 7–19 (1983–1984)

HEISE, G.: Zur Fortpflanzungsbiologie der Rauhhautfledermaus (*Pipistrellus nathusii*). Nyctalus (N.F.) **2,** 1–15 (1984)

HEISE, G. & SCHMIDT, A.: Wo überwintern im Norden der DDR beheimatete Abendsegler (*Nyctalus noctula*)? Nyctalus (N.F.) **1,** 81–84 (1979)

HEU, R.: Mammiferi d'Europa. Arnoldo Mondadori Editore, Milano 1968

HILL, J.E. & SMITH, J.D.: Bats. A Natural History. British Museum, London 1984

HORÁČEK, J. & HANÁK, V. Generic status of *Pipistrellus savii* and comments on classification of the genus *Pipistrellus* (Chiroptera, Vespertilionidae). Myotis **23–24,** 9–16 (1986)

KÖNIG, C.: Wildlebende Säugetiere Europas. Verl. Ch. Belser, Stuttgart 1976

KOLB, A.: Die Geburt einer Fledermaus. Image **49,** 5–13 (1972)

KULZER, E.: Die Herztätigkeit bei lethargischen und winterschlafenden Fledermäusen. Zeitschr. f. vergl. Physiologie **56,** 63–94 (1967)

KULZER, E.: Winterschlaf. Stuttg. Beitr. z. Naturk., Ser. C, H. 14, Staatl. Museum f. Naturkunde, Stuttgart 1981

KURSKOV, A.N.: Bats of Byelorussia. 'Nauka i Technika', Minsk 1981 (Russian)

KUZYAKIN, A.P.: Letuchie myshi (Fledermäuse). Izd. Sovetskaya Nauka, Moskva 1950 (Russian)

MASING, M.: Lendlased (Fledermäuse). 'Valgus' Tallin 1984 (Estonian)

MÖHRES, P.: Bildhören – eine neuentdeckte Sinnesleistung der Tiere. Umschau, **60,** 673–678 (1960)

NATUSCHKE, G.: Heimische Fledermäuse. Neue Brehm Bücherei H. 269. A. Ziemsen Verl. Wittenberg 1960

NEUWEILER, G.: Die Ultraschalljäger. GEO, Nr. 1, (Hamburg) 98–113 (1981)

NEUWEILER, G.: Echoortung, S. 708–722. In: Hoppe, W. et al. (Herausg.): Biophysik, 2. Aufl., Springer Verl., Berlin, Heidelberg, New York 1982

PELIKÁN, J., GAISLER, J. & RÖDL, P.: Näsi savci. Academia, Praha 1979

PUCEK, Z. (Ed.): Keys to Vertebrates of Poland.

Mammals. PWN – Polish Scientific Publishers, Warszawa 1981

ROER, H.: Zur Bestandsentwicklung einiger Fledermäuse in Mitteleuropa. Myotis **18–19**, 60–67 (1980–1981)

ROER, H. (Publisher): Berichte und Ergebnisse von Markierungsversuchen an Fledermäusen in Europa. Decheniana, 18. Beiheft, Bonn 1971

RYBERG, O.: Studies on bats and bat parasites, Svensk Nature, Stockholm 1947

SCHILLING, D., SINGER, D. & DILLER, H.: Säugetiere. BLV-Verlagsgesellschaft, München, Wien, Zürich 1983

SCHMIDT, U.: Vampirfledermäuse. Neue Brehm Bücherei H. 515. A Ziemsen Verl. Wittenberg 1978

SCHRÖPFER, R., FELDMANN, R. UND VIERHAUS, H. (Publisher): Die Säugetiere Westfalens. Westfälisches Mus. f. Naturk., Landschaftsverband Westfalen-Lippe, Münster 1984

SCHOBER, W.: Mit Echolot & Ultraschall. Die phantastische Welt der Fledertiere. Herder Verl., Freiburg 1983

SOKOLOV, I.I. (Publisher): Die Säugetierfauna der UdSSR (russ.) Teil 1, Verl. d. Akademie der Wissenschaften d. UdSSR, Moskau – Leningrad 1963

STEBBINGS, R.E.: Conservation of European Bats. Christopher Helm, London 1988

STEBBINGS, R.E. & WALSH, S.T.: Bat Boxes; a Guide to their History, Function, Construction and Use in the Conservation of Bats. 2nd Edition. Fauna and Flora Preservation Society, London 1988

TOSCHI, A. i LANZA B.: Fauna d'Italia. Vol. IV: Mammalia. Edizioni Calderini, Bologna 1959

TUPINIER, Y.: Description d'une chauve-souris nouvelle: *Myotis nathalinae* nov. spec. (Chiroptera-Vespertilionidae). Mammalia **41**, 327–340 (1977)

YALDEN, B.W. & MORRIS, P.A.: The Lives of Bats. David and Charles, Newton Abbot, London, Vancouver 1975

Bat Journals

MYOTIS – Publisher: Zoolog. Forschungsinstitut u. Museum A. Koenig BRD – 5300 Bonn.

NYCTALUS – Publisher: Tierpark Berlin (Prof. Dr. Dr. Dathe). DDR – 1136 Berlin.

BAT NEWS – Publisher: Fauna and Flora Preservation Soc., c/o Zoolog. Soc. of London, Regents Park, London NW1 4RY.

BATS – Publisher: Bat Conservation International, P.O. Box 162 630 Austin, Texas 78716-2603 USA.

Index

Barbastella barbastellus 173–176
Barbastelle 173–176
Bat boxes 30, 77–78
Bat detector 37, 84
Bechstein's bat 126–128
Behaviour 52, 54, 56–57
Births 44–45, 48
Birth weight 48
Blasius's horseshoe bat 98–99
Body temperature 21, 59, 63–65
Brandt's bat 113–115
Breathing 21, 62

Calcar 16
Calls 36–42, 84–85, 87, 103
Catching methods 71
Cave-dwelling bats 27, 28, 30
Cluster 65, 67

Daubenton's bat 104–107
Detector 37, 84
Diet 12–13, 31, 33–36, 83–84
Drinking 32
Droppings 35

Ears 22, 86
Echolocation 31–42, 84, 103
Embryonic development 21, 44, 51
Enemies 73
Eptesicus nilssonii 147–149
Eptesicus serotinus 143–146
European free-tailed bat 181–183
Evolution 13, 15
Eyes 22, 42

False nipples 24, 87
Flight 16–17, 19, 20, 33, 103
Flight membrane 16, 22
Flying foxes 12, 14
Fossils 15
Free-tailed bats 181, 193

Geoffroy's bat 120–122
Greater horseshoe bat 92–94
Greater mouse-eared bat 129–131
Greater noctule 141–142
Grey long-eared bat 170–172
Grooming 54

Hair 23, 24
Harem 42
Heat regulation 59, 63–65
Hibernation 57–62, 64, 65–67
Hind legs 16–17, 18
Horseshoe bats 20, 22, 86–87, 187
House-dwelling bat 27
Hunting flight 31–33
Hunting territory 32

Juveniles 50, 59

Keeping in captivity 78–79
Kuhl's pipistrelle bat 161–162

Leisler's bat 138–140
Lesser horseshoe bat 88–91
Lesser mouse-eared bat 132–133
Life expectancy 44
Long-eared bat 166–169
Long-fingered bat 108–109

Mammary glands 24, 87, 103
Mating 42–43, 66
Mediterranean horseshoe bat 95–97
Mehely's horseshoe bat 100–102
Metabolism 20–21, 62
Migration 25, 69, 83
Miniopterus schreibersii 177–180
Myotis bechsteinii 126–128
Myotis blythi 132–133
Myotis brandtii 113–115
Myotis capaccinii 108–109
Myotis dasycneme 110–112
Myotis daubentonii 104–107
Myotis emarginatus 120–122
Myotis myotis 129–131
Myotis mystacinus 116–119
Myotis nattereri 123–125

Nathusius' pipistrelle 158–160
Natterer's bat 123–125
Noctule bat 134–137
Northern bat 147–149
Nose leaves 22, 86
Nursery roosts 25, 28, 30, 44–45
Nyctalus lasiopterus 141–142
Nyctalus leisleri 138–140
Nyctalus noctula 134–137

Parasites   73
Parti-coloured bat   150–152
Pest control   35–36
Pipistrelle   153–157
Pipistrellus kuhli   161–162
Pipistrellus nathusii   158–160
Pipistrellus pipistrellus   153–157
Pipistrellus savii   163–165
Plecotus auritus   166–169
Plecotus austriacus   170–172
Pond bat   110–112
Post-calcarial lobe   16
Protection   73–78, 83

Rabies   73
Reproduction   42, 83
Rhinolophus blasii   98–99
Rhinolophus euryale   95–97
Rhinolophus ferrumequinum   92–94
Rhinolophus hipposideros   88–91
Rhinolophus mehelyi   100–102
Ringing   70–72
Roost protection and artificial roosts   75–78
Roosts   25–30, 42

Savi's pipistrelle   163–165

Schreiber's bat   177–180
Sensory hairs   42
Serotine   143–146
Sexes   23–24
Skeleton   16–17, 194–195
Skin glands   22–23
Smell   34, 42
Social thermoregulation   65
Sonagram   37, 85, 210–213
Superstition   8, 10
Systematics   11–13, 86–87, 103, 216–219

Tadarida teniotis   181–183
Tail membrane   16, 86–87, 103
Teeth   22, 50, 87, 103
Threats to bats   73–74
Tragus   22
Tree-dwelling bats   28

Ultrasound   33, 34–35, 36–39, 41

Vampire bats   12–13
Vesper bats   18, 22, 103, 188–193
Vespertilio murinus   150–152

Whiskered bat   116–119
Wood preservatives   74, 76